COLLINS CLASSICS COLLECTION

THE WORLD ACCORDING TO DICKENS

Matters of Life and Death

MIKE RUSSELL

General Editor: Geoff Fox

CollinsEducational
An imprint of HarperCollins*Publishers*

For my mother and father whose love for Dickens nurtured my own.

ISBN 0 00 323035 X

First published by CollinsEducational, *an imprint of* HarperCollins *Publishers* 77–85 Fulham Palace Road, London W6 8JB.

Cover and text designed by Christie Archer

Cover illustration by Neil Dishington

Edited by Stephen Attmore

Production by James Graves

Typeset by Wyvern Typesetting Limited

Printed by Scotprint Ltd, Musselburgh

Acknowledgements

The author and publishers would like to thank the following for permission to reproduce illustrations:

The Bridgeman Art Library: p. 130; The Dickens House Museum: pp. 4, 13, 21, 48, 56, 60, 63, 64, 84, 100, 108, 113, 136, 173, 182; Dover Publications: pp. 134, 162, 170; Illustrated London News Picture Library: p. 11; Mansell Collection: pp. 117, 132.

CONTENTS

CRIME AND PUNISHMENT

Charles Dickens (1812–1870)

"Depend upon it he was quite a self-made man, and his wonderful knowledge and command of the English language must have been acquired by long and patient study after leaving his last school"; that is how a fellow-pupil at Wellington House Academy (which Dickens attended between the ages of thirteen and fifteen) described the famous author he used to share penny magazines with as a boy and join begging in the streets of London just to annoy passers-by.

We know a great deal about the Dickens who became famous at twenty-four and stayed firmly in the public eye as a journalist, novelist, speech maker, reformer, supporter of numerous charities, fund-raiser for Great Ormond Street Children's Hospital, editor, gifted amateur actor, spell-binding reader of his own stories to packed houses up and down the country, and about a host of other activities that Dickens's enormous energy found outlets for. About his early years we know much less.

Dickens was born in Portsmouth, the son of John Dickens who worked in the Navy Pay Office. The family was regularly on the move, to London, to Chatham, back to London again. This was partly because of John Dickens's job but also because Charles's father was constantly getting into debt, just as Mr Micawber does in *David Copperfield*; Dickens put a lot of his father into this character.

The schooling of the young Dickens was irregular and there was one long interruption which Dickens only referred to many years later. When he was twelve and the family was once again in financial trouble, Charles was sent to work at Warren's blacking-warehouse to paste labels onto bottles. Dickens so deeply resented this menial job that it seemed to have left a permanent scar, perhaps because it coincided with John Dickens being arrested for debt and sent to the Marshalsea Prison where there was room for all the family to live except Charles. The father was released in three months but the son, experiencing his own form of imprisonment, may have worked in the warehouse for as much as a year or even a little more – a long time when you are only twelve.

It is perhaps not surprising that prisons figure largely in Dickens's novels or that the books should be thickly populated with irresponsible and incompetent parents and ill-used children. Part of *David Copperfield* touches directly on the warehouse episode when David feels something of the pain and resentment that the author experienced, though in the fictional version it is difficult not to feel that David is suffering because he is over-sensitive and a bit "prissy". Dickens does a better job of re-creating the world of the child elsewhere in the book.

When Dickens went back to school at thirteen it seems to have done little for him, if his classmate's memory of Wellington House is accurate, and at fifteen he left. How Dickens got his education is something of a mystery. He had a small collection of books as a child that included the *Arabian Nights* and a number of eighteenth century adventure stories (see page 16, where David Copperfield refers to a collection that partly coincides with Dickens's own). The suggestion that Dickens was self-educated looks to be the right one.

At any rate, when fifteen, he was employable enough to be a solicitors' clerk; by seventeen he had mastered a fiendishly difficult system of shorthand and was working as a freelance reporter. Two years later, Dickens was covering parliamentary proceedings for a newspaper and earning a reputation for speed and accuracy.

For leisure, Dickens records how he went to the theatre most nights of the week. Because there were only three London Theatres licensed for "straight" plays – Covent Garden, Drury Lane and the Haymarket – he must have enjoyed the melodramas, music hall entertainments and the private theatre (where amateur actors could try their hand at playing Hamlet, for example) as well.

By twenty, Dickens knew Shakespeare well enough to quote him naturally and without showing-off in letters to friends, and seems to have learned French. Just as importantly, his fondness for long walks, often at night, gave him a detailed knowledge of London and of city life that few people could have matched. In 1833, when he was twenty-one, Dickens's first story, 'A Dinner at Poplar Walk' was published, in the *Monthly Magazine*, which did not pay its contributors; but it was an opening and Dickens followed up with a number of other stories. He could call himself an author now, not just a reporter, though he stayed one until his first two books, *Sketches by Boz* (Boz was the childhood nickname of his younger brother) and *The Pickwick Papers* proved successful.

The Pickwick Papers rapidly reached cult status and it was important in another respect: Dickens published it in serial form, which was a cheap method of publication. This gave him a wider readership and closer contact with his readers. As each monthly number came out he could tell from the sales and the responses of friends and readers who wrote to him how his developing book was being received. All of Dickens's novels were serialised and many other novelists followed his example.

Oliver Twist was begun while *The Pickwick Papers* was being written, then followed *Nicholas Nickleby, The Old Curiosity Shop* and the first historical novel, *Barnaby Rudge*; five books in as many years, and Dickens was still only twenty-nine.

In the 1840s, Dickens visited America recording his impressions in *American Notes*. In the same period, he wrote *Martin Chuzzlewit* and the first of his Christmas books, *A Christmas Carol*, started a newspaper (*The Daily News*) and then embarked on the first of his more serious novels, *Dombey and Son*.

In the 1850s, Dickens started a weekly journal, *Household Words*, and began a new novel, *David Copperfield*, in which the hero tells the story of his life, and which has associations in several places with Dickens's own.

Some of the greatest novels were still to come and Dickens's deepening social concern and developing artistry made *Bleak House, Hard Times, Little Dorrit, Great Expectations*, and *Our Mutual Friend* the most challenging of his novels (the exception, perhaps, in this group being *A Tale of Two Cities* which seems melodramatic alongside the others).

Dickens's last novel, *The Mystery of Edwin Drood*, was never completed. At his home in Gad's Hill in Kent, close to where he spent his early childhood, Dickens suffered a stroke and died while working on the book. He was fifty-eight.

There is no easy way of summing up Dickens's achievement, but one tribute from the Russian novelist, Leo Tolstoy, points to something that many readers have felt when he said of Dickens that, "all his characters are my personal friends". Dickens's ability to invent a vast number of memorable characters is one of the reasons why his fiction is part of our folklore: people know about Mr. Micawber as they know about Hamlet, even without having read *David Copperfield* or Shakespeare's play.

A popularity on a world-wide scale that has lasted over a hundred and fifty years can be trusted, and the number of radio and television serialisations, films and musicals, too, proves that Dickens speaks to our age as he did so vibrantly to his own.

New readers can feel confident that Dickens has much to offer them as well.

GROWING UP

Pip in the churchyard

Pip is the first of a number of orphans or abandoned children found on these pages. This is the beginning of ***Great Expectations****, Dickens's thirteenth novel and the second in which the hero is also the narrator (the first was* ***David Copperfield****). The novel starts in the Kent marshes where Pip is brought up by his sister and her husband, Joe Gargery, a village blacksmith. In the churchyard where his parents are buried, Pip has an encounter with a man who is to prove very important in Pip's life.*

MY FATHER's family name being Pirrip, and my christian name Philip, my infant tongue could make of both names nothing longer or more explicit than Pip. So, I called myself Pip, and came to be called Pip.

I give Pirrip as my father's family name, on the authority of his tombstone and my sister – Mrs. Joe Gargery, who married the blacksmith. As I never saw my father or my mother, and never saw any likeness of either of them (for their days were long before the days of photographs), my first fancies regarding what they were like, were unreasonably derived from their tombstones. The shape of the letters on my father's, gave me an odd idea that he was a square, stout, dark man, with curly black hair. From the character and turn of the inscription, "*Also Georgiana Wife of the Above*," I drew a childish conclusion that my mother was freckled and sickly. To five little stone lozenges, each about a foot and a half long*, which were arranged in a neat row beside their grave, and were sacred to the memory of five little brothers of mine – who gave up trying to get a living exceedingly early in that universal struggle – I am indebted for a belief I religiously entertained that they had all been born on their backs with their hands in their trousers-pockets, and had never taken them out in this state of existence.

Ours was the marsh country, down by the river, within, as the river wound, twenty miles of the sea. My first most vivid and broad impression of the identity of things, seems to me to have been gained on a memorable raw afternoon towards evening. At such a time I found out for certain, that this bleak place overgrown with nettles was the churchyard; and that Philip Pirrip, late of this parish, and Also Georgiana Wife

* a foot and a half = 18 inches = 45.7 cm

of the Above, were dead and buried; and that Alexander, Bartholomew, Abraham, Tobias, and Roger, infant children of the aforesaid, were also dead and buried; and that the dark flat wilderness beyond the churchyard, intersected with dykes and mounds and gates, with scattered cattle feeding on it, was the marshes; and that the low leaden line beyond, was the river; and that the distant savage lair from which the wind was rushing, was the sea; and that the small bundle of shivers growing afraid of it all and beginning to cry, was Pip.

"Hold your noise!" cried a terrible voice, as a man started up from among the graves at the side of the church porch. "Keep still, you little devil, or I'll cut your throat!"

A fearful man, all in coarse grey, with a great iron on his leg. A man with no hat, and with broken shoes, and with an old rag tied round his head. A man who had been soaked in water, and smothered in mud, and lamed by stones, and cut by flints, and stung by nettles, and torn by briars; who limped, and shivered, and glared and growled; and whose teeth chattered in his head as he seized me by the chin.

"O! Don't cut my throat, sir," I pleaded in terror. "Pray don't do it, sir."

"Tell us your name!" said the man. "Quick!"

"Pip, sir."

"Once more," said the man, staring at me. "Give it mouth!"

"Pip. Pip, sir."

"Show us where you live," said the man. "Pint out the place!"

I pointed to where our village lay, on the flat in-shore among the alder-trees and pollards, a mile or more from the church.

The man, after looking at me for a moment, turned me upside down, and emptied my pockets. There was nothing in them but a piece of bread. When the church came to itself – for he was so sudden and strong that he made it go head over heels before me, and I saw the steeple under my feet – when the church came to itself, I say, I was seated on a high tombstone, trembling, while he ate the bread ravenously.

"You young dog," said the man, licking his lips, "what fat cheeks you ha' got."

I believe they were fat, though I was at that time undersized for my years, and not strong.

"Darn Me if I couldn't eat 'em," said the man, with a threatening shake of his head, "and if I han't half a mind to't!"

I earnestly expressed my hope that he wouldn't, and held tighter to the tombstone on which he had put me; partly, to keep myself upon it; partly, to keep myself from crying.

"Now lookee here!" said the man. "Where's your mother?"

"There, sir!" said I.

The man threatens Pip

He started, made a short run, and stopped and looked over his shoulder.

"There, sir!" I timidly explained. "Also Georgiana. That's my mother."

"Oh!" said he, coming back. "And is that your father alonger your mother?"

"Yes, sir," said I; "him too; late of this parish."

"Ha!" he muttered then, considering. "Who d'ye live with – supposin' you're kindly let to live, which I han't made up my mind about?"

"My sister, sir – Mrs. Joe Gargery – wife of Joe Gargery, the blacksmith, sir."

"Blacksmith, eh?" said he. And looked down at his leg.

After darkly looking at his leg and me several times, he came closer to my tombstone, took me by both arms, and tilted me back as far as he could hold me; so that his eyes looked most powerfully down into mine, and mine looked most helplessly up into his.

"Now lookee here," he said, "the question being whether you're to be let to live. You know what a file is?"

"Yes, sir."

"And you know what wittles* is?"

"Yes, sir."

After each question he tilted me over a little more, so as to give me a greater sense of helplessness and danger.

"You get me a file." He tilted me again. "And you get me wittles." He tilted me again. "You bring 'em both to me." He tilted me again. "Or I'll have your heart and liver out." He tilted me again.

I was dreadfully frightened, and so giddy that I clung to him with both hands, and said, "If you would kindly please to let me keep upright, sir, perhaps I shouldn't be sick, and perhaps I could attend more."

He gave me a most tremendous dip and roll, so that the church jumped over its own weather-cock. Then, he held me by the arms, in an upright position on the top of the stone, and went on in these fearful terms:

"You bring me, tomorrow morning early, that file and them wittles. You bring the lot to me, at that old Battery* over yonder. You do it, and you never dare to say a word or dare to make a sign concerning your having seen such a person as me, or any person sumever, and you shall be let to live. You fail, or you go from my words in any partickler, no matter how small it is, and your heart and your liver shall be tore out, roasted and ate. Now, I ain't alone, as you may think I am. There's a young man hid with me, in comparison with which young man I am a Angel. That young man hears the words I speak. That young man has a secret way pecooliar to himself, of getting at a boy, and at his heart, and at his liver. It is in wain for a boy to attempt to hide himself from that young man. A boy may lock his door, may be warm in bed, may tuck himself up, may draw the clothes over his head, may think himself comfortable and safe, but that young man will softly creep and creep his way to him and tear him open. I am a keeping that young man from harming of you at the present moment, with great difficulty. I find it very hard to hold that young man off of your inside. Now, what do you say?"

I said that I would get him the file, and I would get him what broken bits of food I could, and I would come to him at the Battery, early in the morning.

"Say, Lord strike you dead if you don't!" said the man.

* wittles: victuals (food)

* Battery: a defensive position or emplacement guarding the approach to London from the sea.

I said so, and he took me down.

"Now," he pursued, "you remember what you've undertook, and you remember that young man, and you get home!"

"Goo-good night, sir," I faltered.

"Much of that!" said he, glancing about him over the cold wet flat. "I wish I was a frog. Or a eel!"

At the same time, he hugged his shuddering body in both his arms – clasping himself, as if to hold himself together – and limped towards the low church wall. As I saw him go, picking his way among the nettles, and among the brambles that bound the green mounds, he looked in my young eyes as if he were eluding the hands of the dead people, stretching up cautiously out of their graves, to get a twist upon his ankle and pull him in.

When he came to the low church wall, he got over it, like a man whose legs were numbed and stiff, and then turned round to look for me. When I saw him turning, I set my face towards home, and made the best use of my legs. But presently I looked over my shoulder, and saw him going on again towards the river, still hugging himself in both arms, and picking his way with his sore feet among the great stones dropped into the marshes here and there, for stepping-places when the rains were heavy, or the tide was in.

The marshes were just a long black horizontal line then, as I stopped to look after him; and the river was just another horizontal line, not nearly so broad nor yet so black; and the sky was just a row of long angry red lines and dense black lines intermixed. On the edge of the river I could faintly make out the only two black things in all the prospect that seemed to be standing upright; one of these was the beacon by which the sailors steered – like an unhooped cask upon a pole – an ugly thing when you were near it; the other a gibbet, with some chains hanging to it which had once held a pirate. The man was limping on towards this latter, as if he were the pirate come to life, and come down, and going back to hook himself up again. It gave me a terrible turn when I thought so; and as I saw the cattle lifting their heads to gaze after him, I wondered whether they thought so too. I looked all round for the horrible young man, and could see no signs of him. But, now I was frightened again, and ran home without stopping.

Great Expectations, *Chapter 1*

Early memories

This is an early chapter from ***David Copperfield****, which Dickens used to refer to as his "favourite child". It is often assumed that this is the author's most autobiographical novel. David tells his own story and here goes back to early childhood memories.*

THE first objects that assume a distinct presence before me, as I look far back, into the blank of my infancy, are my mother with her pretty hair and youthful shape, and Peggotty* with no shape at all, and eyes so dark that they seemed to darken their whole neighbourhood in her face, and cheeks and arms so hard and red that I wondered the birds didn't peck her in preference to apples.

I believe I can remember these two at a little distance apart, dwarfed to my sight by stooping down or kneeling on the floor, and I going unsteadily from the one to the other. I have an impression on my mind which I cannot distinguish from actual remembrance, of the touch of Peggotty's forefinger as she used to hold it out to me, and of its being roughened by needlework, like a pocket nutmeg-grater.

This may be fancy, though I think the memory of most of us can go farther back into such times than many of us suppose; just as I believe the power of observation in numbers of very young children to be quite wonderful for its closeness and accuracy. Indeed, I think that most grown men who are remarkable in this respect, may with greater propriety be said not to have lost the faculty, than to have acquired it; the rather, as I generally observe such men to retain a certain freshness, and gentleness, and capacity of being pleased, which are also an inheritance they have preserved from their childhood.

I might have a misgiving that I am "meandering" in stopping to say this, but that it brings me to remark that I build these conclusions, in part upon my own experience of myself; and if it should appear from anything I may set down in this narrative that I was a child of close observation, or that as a man I have a strong memory of my childhood, I undoubtedly lay claim to both of these characteristics.

Looking back, as I was saying, into the blank of my infancy, the first objects I can remember as standing out by themselves from a confusion

* Peggotty: the family servant

of things, are my mother and Peggotty. What else do I remember? Let me see.

There comes out of the cloud, our house – not new to me, but quite familiar, in its earliest remembrance. On the ground-floor is Peggotty's kitchen, opening into a back yard; with a pigeon-house on a pole, in the centre, without any pigeons in it; a great dog-kennel in a corner, without any dog; and a quantity of fowls that look terribly tall to me, walking about, in a menacing and ferocious manner. There is one cock who gets upon a post to crow, and seems to take particular notice of me as I look at him through the kitchen window, who makes me shiver, he is so fierce. Of the geese outside the side-gate who come waddling after me with their long necks stretched out when I go that way, I dream at night: as a man environed by wild beasts might dream of lions.

Here is a long passage – what an enormous perspective I make of it – leading from Peggotty's kitchen to the front door. A dark store-room opens out of it, and that is a place to be run past at night; for I don't know what may be among those tubs and jars and old tea-chests, when there is nobody in there with a dimly burning light, letting a mouldy air come out of the door, in which there is the smell of soap, pickles, pepper, candles, and coffee, all at one whiff. Then there are the two parlours: the parlour in which we sit of an evening, my mother and I and Peggotty – for Peggotty is quite our companion, when her work is done and we are alone – and the best parlour where we sit on a Sunday; grandly, but not so comfortably. There is something of a doleful air about that room to me, for Peggotty has told me – I don't know when, but apparently ages ago – about my father's funeral, and the company having their black cloaks put on. One Sunday night my mother reads to Peggotty and me in there, how Lazarus was raised up from the dead*. And I am so frightened that they are afterwards obliged to take me out of bed, and show me the quiet churchyard out of the bedroom window, with the dead all lying in their graves at rest, below the solemn moon.

David Copperfield, *Chapter 2*

* Lazarus: raised from the dead by Jesus (*John, 11*)

Oliver in the workhouse

Dickens was still writing **The Pickwick Papers** *when he began* **Oliver Twist**, *the story of a workhouse orphan. Workhouses were built for the destitute poor and conditions there were made deliberately harsh so as to ensure it was not an easy alternative to working.*

Oliver Twist has spent the first eight years of his life in a branch workhouse, or baby farm, for very young orphans. Now, on his ninth birthday, he is brought to a main workhouse so that a parish board can decide his future; which means, Dickens makes clear, putting him to work on starvation rations.

"Boy," said the gentleman in the high chair, "listen to me. You know you're an orphan, I suppose?"

"What's that, sir?" inquired poor Oliver.

"The boy *is* a fool – I thought he was," said the gentleman in the white waistcoat, in a very decided tone. If one member of a class be blessed with an intuitive perception of others of the same race, the gentleman in the white waistcoat was unquestionably well qualified to pronounce an opinion on the matter.

"Hush!" said the gentleman who had spoken first. "You know you've got no father or mother, and that you were brought up by the parish, don't you?"

"Yes, sir," replied Oliver, weeping bitterly.

"What are you crying for?" inquired the gentleman in the white waistcoat. And to be sure it was very extraordinary. What *could* the boy be crying for?

"I hope you say your prayers every night," said another gentleman in a gruff voice; "and pray for the people who feed you, and take care of you – like a Christian."

"Yes, sir," stammered the boy. The gentleman who spoke last was unconsciously right. It would have been *very* like a Christian, and a marvellously good Christian, too, if Oliver had prayed for the people who fed and took care of *him*. But he hadn't, because nobody had taught him.

"Well! You have come here to be educated, and taught a useful trade," said the red-faced gentleman in the high chair.

"So you'll begin to pick oakum* tomorrow morning at six o'clock," added the surly one in the white waistcoat.

For the combination of both these blessings in the one simple process of picking oakum, Oliver bowed low by the direction of the beadle*, and was then hurried away to a large ward: where, on a rough, hard bed, he sobbed himself to sleep. What a noble illustration of the tender laws of this favoured country! They let the paupers go to sleep!

Poor Oliver! He little thought, as he lay sleeping in happy unconsciousness of all around him, that the board had that very day arrived at a decision which would exercise the most material influence over all his future fortunes. But they had. And this was it:

The members of this board were very sage, deep, philosophical men, and when they came to turn their attention to the workhouse, they found out at once, what ordinary folks would never have discovered – the poor people liked it! It was a regular place of public entertainment for the poorer classes; a tavern where there was nothing to pay; a public breakfast, dinner, tea, and supper all the year round; a brick and mortar elysium, where it was all play and no work. "Oho!" said the board, looking very knowing; "we are the fellows to set this to rights; we'll stop it all, in no time." So, they established the rule, that all poor people should have the alternative (for they would compel nobody, not they), of being starved by a gradual process in the house, or by a quick one out of it. With this view, they contracted with the water-works to lay on an unlimited supply of water; and with a corn-factor to supply periodically small quantities of oatmeal; and issued three meals of thin gruel a day, with an onion twice a week, and half a roll on Sundays. They made a great many other wise and humane regulations having reference to the ladies, which it is not necessary to repeat; kindly undertook to divorce poor married people, in consequence of the great expense of a suit in Doctors' Commons*; and, instead of compelling a man to support his family, as they had theretofore done, took his family away from him, and made him a bachelor! There is no saying how many applicants for relief, under these last two heads, might have started up in all classes of society, if it had not been coupled with the workhouse; but the board were long-headed men, and had provided for this difficulty. The relief was inseparable from the workhouse and the gruel; and that frightened people.

* oakum: the combings of old ropes used for caulking: a task set for paupers and convicts.

* beadle: a low-ranking officer of parishes and law-courts in Dickens's time. The author's view of them may be inferred from the name of this one – Mr. Bumble.

* Doctors' Commons: a college of lawyers that handled marriage licences, divorces and probates on wills. Dickens's early experiences, as a reporter, of the creaking operations of this particular limb of the law led to the "Doctors' Commons" article in *Sketches by Boz* and a lifelong hostility to the many inefficiencies within the legal system.

A typical workhouse

For the first six months after Oliver Twist was removed, the system was in full operation. It was rather expensive at first, in consequence of the increase in the undertaker's bill, and the necessity of taking in the clothes of all the paupers, which fluttered loosely on their wasted, shrunken forms, after a week or two's gruel. But the number of workhouse inmates got thin as well as the paupers; and the board were in ecstasies.

The room in which the boys were fed was a large stone hall, with a copper at one end; out of which the master, dressed in an apron for the purpose, and assisted by one or two women, ladled the gruel at mealtimes; of which composition each boy had one porringer*, and no more – except on festive occasions, and then he had two ounces and a quarter* of bread besides. The bowls never wanted washing. The boys polished them with their spoons till they shone again; and when they had performed this operation (which never took very long, the spoons being nearly as large as the bowls), they would sit staring at the copper with such eager eyes as if they could have devoured the very bricks of which it was composed; employing themselves, meanwhile, in sucking their fingers most assiduously, with the view of catching up any stray splashes of gruel that might have been cast thereon. Boys have generally excellent appetites. Oliver Twist and his companions suffered the tortures of slow

* porringer: a small dish

* two ounces and a quarter = 64 grams

starvation for three months: at last they got so voracious and wild with hunger, that one boy, who was tall for his age, and hadn't been used to that sort of thing (for his father had kept a small cookshop), hinted darkly to his companions, that unless he had another basin of gruel *per diem**, he was afraid he might some night happen to eat the boy who slept next him, who happened to be a weakly youth of tender age. He had a wild, hungry eye; and they implicitly believed him. A council was held; lots were cast who should walk up to the master after supper that evening, and ask for more; and it fell to Oliver Twist.

The evening arrived; the boys took their places. The master, in his cook's uniform, stationed himself at the copper; his pauper assistants ranged themselves behind him; the gruel was served out; and a long grace was said over the short commons. The gruel disappeared; the boys whispered each other, and winked at Oliver, while his next neighbours nudged him. Child as he was, he was desperate with hunger, and reckless with misery. He rose from the table, and advancing to the master, basin and spoon in hand, said: somewhat alarmed at his own temerity:

"Please, sir, I want some more."

The master was a fat, healthy man; but he turned very pale. He gazed in stupefied astonishment on the small rebel for some seconds, and then clung for support to the copper. The assistants were paralysed with wonder; the boys with fear.

"What!" said the master at length, in a faint voice.

"Please, sir," replied Oliver, "I want some more."

The master aimed a blow at Oliver's head with the ladle, pinioned him in his arms; and shrieked aloud for the beadle.

The board were sitting in solemn conclave, when Mr. Bumble rushed into the room in great excitement, and addressing the gentleman in the high chair, said,

"Mr. Limbkins, I beg your pardon, sir! Oliver Twist has asked for more!" There was a general start. Horror was depicted on every countenance.

"For *more*!" said Mr. Limbkins. "Compose yourself, Bumble, and answer me distinctly. Do I understand that he asked for more, after he had eaten the supper allotted by the dietary?"

"He did, sir," replied Bumble.

"That boy will be hung," said the gentleman in the white waistcoat; "I know that boy will be hung."

Nobody controverted the prophetic gentleman's opinion. An animated discussion took place. Oliver was ordered into instant confinement; and a bill was next morning pasted on the outside of the gate, offering a reward of five pounds to anybody who would take Oliver

* *per diem*: a day

Oliver asking for more

Twist off the hands of the parish. In other words, five pounds and Oliver Twist were offered to any man or woman who wanted an apprentice to any trade, business, or calling.

"I never was more convinced of anything in my life," said the gentleman in the white waistcoat, as he knocked at the gate and read the bill next morning: "I never was more convinced of anything in my life, than I am that that boy will come to be hung."

Oliver Twist, *Chapter 2*

David and his stepfather

David Copperfield's widowed mother marries the darkly handsome but sadistic Mr. Murdstone who, with his stern sister, quickly dominates the Copperfield household. One of Dickens's gifts is his ability to invent evocative names for his characters and Murdstone lives up to his.

THERE had been some talk on occasions of my going to boarding-school. Mr. and Miss Murdstone had originated it, and my mother had of course agreed with them. Nothing, however, was concluded on the subject yet. In the meantime, I learnt lessons at home.

Shall I ever forget those lessons! They were presided over nominally by my mother, but really by Mr. Murdstone and his sister, who were always present, and found them a favourable occasion for giving my mother lessons in that miscalled firmness, which was the bane of both our lives. . . . .

Let me remember how it used to be, and bring one morning back again.

I come into the second-best parlour after breakfast, with my books, and an exercise-book, and a slate. My mother is ready for me at her writing-desk, but not half so ready as Mr. Murdstone in his easy-chair by the window (though he pretends to be reading a book), or as Miss Murdstone, sitting near my mother stringing steel beads. The very sight of these two has such an influence over me, that I begin to feel the words I have been at infinite pains to get into my head, all sliding away, and going I don't know where. I wonder where they *do* go, by the by?

I hand the first book to my mother. Perhaps it is a grammar, perhaps a history, or geography. I take a last drowning look at the page as I give it into her hand, and start off aloud at a racing pace while I have got it fresh. I trip over a word. Mr. Murdstone looks up. I trip over another word. Miss Murdstone looks up. I redden, tumble over half-a-dozen words, and stop. I think my mother would show me the book if she dared, but she does not dare, and she says softly:

"Oh, Davy, Davy!"

"Now, Clara," says Mr. Murdstone, "be firm with the boy. Don't say, 'Oh, Davy, Davy!' That's childish. He knows his lesson, or he does not know it."

"He does *not* know it," Miss Murdstone interposes awfully.

"I am really afraid he does not," says my mother.

"Then, you see, Clara," returns Miss Murdstone, "you should just give him the book back, and make him know it."

"Yes, certainly," says my mother; "that is what I intend to do, my dear Jane. Now, Davy, try once more, and don't be stupid."

I obey the first clause of the injunction by trying once more, but am not so successful with the second, for I am very stupid. I tumble down before I get to the old place, at a point where I was all right before, and stop to think. But I can't think about the lesson. I think of the number of yards of net in Miss Murdstone's cap, or of the price of Mr. Murdstone's dressing-gown, or any such ridiculous problem that I have no business with, and don't want to have anything at all to do with. Mr. Murdstone makes a movement of impatience which I have been expecting for a long time. Miss Murdstone does the same. My mother glances submissively at them, shuts the book, and lays it by as an arrear to be worked out when my other tasks are done.

There is a pile of these arrears very soon, and it swells like a rolling snowball. The bigger it gets, the more stupid *I* get. The case is so hopeless, and I feel that I am wallowing in such a bog of nonsense, that I give up all idea of getting out, and abandon myself to my fate. The despairing way in which my mother and I look at each other, as I blunder on, is truly melancholy. But the greatest effect in these miserable lessons is when my mother (thinking nobody is observing her) tries to give me the cue by the motion of her lips. At that instant, Miss Murdstone, who has been lying in wait for nothing else all along, says in a deep warning voice:

"Clara!"

My mother starts, colours, and smiles faintly. Mr. Murdstone comes out of his chair, takes the book, throws it at me or boxes my ears with it, and turns me out of the room by the shoulders.

Even when the lessons are done, the worst is yet to happen, in the shape of an appalling sum. This is invented for me, and delivered to me orally by Mr. Murdstone, and begins, "If I go into a cheesemonger's shop, and buy five thousand double-Gloucester cheeses at fourpence-halfpenny each, present payment" – at which I see Miss Murdstone secretly overjoyed. I pore over these cheeses without any result or enlightenment until dinner-time, when, having made a Mulatto* of myself by getting the dirt of the slate into the pores of my skin, I have a slice of bread to help me out with the cheeses, and am considered in disgrace for the rest of the evening.

It seems to me, at this distance of time, as if my unfortunate studies

* Mulatto: half white and half negro

generally took this course. I could have done very well if I had been without the Murdstones; but the influence of the Murdstones upon me was like the fascination of two snakes on a wretched young bird. Even when I did get through the morning with tolerable credit, there was not much gained but dinner; for Miss Murdstone never could endure to see me untasked, and if I rashly made any show of being unemployed, called her brother's attention to me by saying, "Clara, my dear, there's nothing like work – give your boy an exercise"; which caused me to be clapped down to some new labour, there and then. As to any recreation with other children of my age, I had very little of that; for the gloomy theology of the Murdstones made all children out to be a swarm of little vipers (though there *was* a child once set in the midst of the Disciples*), and held that they contaminated one another.

The natural result of this treatment, continued, I suppose, for some six months or more, was to make me sullen, dull, and dogged. I was not made the less so by my sense of being daily more and more shut out and alienated from my mother. I believe I should have been almost stupefied but for one circumstance.

It was this. My father had left a small collection of books* in a little room upstairs, to which I had access (for it adjoined my own) and which nobody else in our house ever troubled. From that blessed little room, Roderick Random, Peregrine Pickle, Humphrey Clinker, Tom Jones, the Vicar of Wakefield, Don Quixote, Gil Blas, and Robinson Crusoe, came out, a glorious host, to keep me company. They kept alive my fancy, and my hope of something beyond that place and time,– they, and the *Arabian Nights*, and the *Tales of the Genii*, – and did me no harm; for whatever harm was in some of them was not there for me; *I* knew nothing of it. It is astonishing to me now, how I found time, in the midst of my porings and blunderings over heavier themes, to read those books as I did. It is curious to me how I could ever have consoled myself under my small troubles (which were great troubles to me), by impersonating my favourite characters in them – as I did – and by putting Mr. and Miss Murdstone into all the bad ones – which I did too. I have been Tom Jones (a child's Tom Jones, a harmless creature) for a week together. I have sustained my own idea of Roderick Random for a month at a stretch, I verily believe. I had a greedy relish for a few volumes of Voyages and Travels – I forget what, now – that were on those shelves; and for days and days I can remember to have gone about my region of our house, armed with the centre-piece out of an old set of boot-trees –

* Dickens probably had in mind ***Mark*, *9***, verses 35–37, where Christ tells his disciples, "Whosoever shall receive one of such children in my name, receiveth me."

* collection of books: Dickens's father left his son a similar collection of eighteenth-century books. The prominent writer here is Tobias Smollett, the author of the first three novels listed and the translator of *Gil Blas*. These are all adventure stories of one kind or another.

the perfect realisation of Captain Somebody, of the Royal British Navy, in danger of being beset by savages, and resolved to sell his life at a great price. The Captain never lost dignity, from having his ears boxed with the Latin Grammar. I did; but the Captain was a Captain and a hero, in despite of all the grammars of all the languages in the world, dead or alive.

This was my only and my constant comfort. When I think of it, the picture always rises in my mind, of a summer evening, the boys at play in the churchyard, and I sitting on my bed, reading as if for life. Every barn in the neighbourhood, every stone in the church, and every foot of the churchyard, had some association of its own, in my mind, connected with these books, and stood for some locality made famous in them. I have seen Tom Pipes go climbing up the church-steeple; I have watched Strap, with the knapsack on his back, stopping to rest himself upon the wicket-gate; and I *know* that Commodore Trunnion held that club with Mr. Pickle, in the parlour of our little village alehouse.*

One morning when I went into the parlour with my books, I found my mother looking anxious, Miss Murdstone looking firm, and Mr. Murdstone binding something round the bottom of a cane – a lithe and limber cane, which he left off binding when I came in, and poised and switched in the air.

"I tell you, Clara," said Mr. Murdstone, "I have been often flogged myself."

"To be sure; of course," said Miss Murdstone.

"Certainly, my dear Jane," faltered my mother, meekly. "But – but do you think it did Edward good?"

"Do you think it did Edward harm, Clara?" asked Mr. Murdstone, gravely.

"That's the point," said his sister.

To this my mother returned, "Certainly, my dear Jane," and said no more.

I felt apprehensive that I was personally interested in this dialogue, and sought Mr. Murdstone's eye as it lighted on mine.

"Now, David," he said – and I saw that cast again as he said it – "you must be far more careful today than usual." He gave the cane another poise, and another switch; and having finished his preparation of it, laid it down beside him, with an impressive look, and took up his book.

This was a good freshener to my presence of mind, as a beginning. I felt the words of my lessons slipping off, not one by one, or line by line, but by the entire page; I tried to lay hold of them; but they seemed, if I may so express it, to have put skates on, and to skim away from me with a smoothness there was no checking.

* Tom Pipes, etc.: characters in two of Dickens's favourite novels, *Roderick Random* and *Peregrine Pickle*, by Tobias Smollett.

We began badly, and went on worse. I had come in with an idea of distinguishing myself rather, conceiving that I was very well prepared; but it turned out to be quite a mistake. Book after book was added to the heap of failures, Miss Murdstone being firmly watchful of us all the time. And when we came at last to the five thousand cheeses (canes he made it that day, I remember), my mother burst out crying.

"Clara!" said Miss Murdstone, in her warning voice.

"I am not quite well, my dear Jane, I think," said my mother.

I saw him wink, solemnly, at his sister, as he rose and said, taking up the cane:

"Why, Jane, we can hardly expect Clara to bear, with perfect firmness, the worry and torment that David has occasioned her today. That would be stoical. Clara is greatly strengthened and improved, but we can hardly expect so much from her. David, you and I will go upstairs, boy."

As he took me out at the door, my mother ran towards us. Miss Murdstone said, "Clara! are you a perfect fool?" and interfered. I saw my mother stop her ears then, and I heard her crying.

He walked me up to my room slowly and gravely – I am certain he had a delight in that formal parade of executing justice – and when we got there, suddenly twisted my head under his arm.

"Mr. Murdstone! Sir!" I cried to him. "Don't! Pray don't beat me! I have tried to learn, sir, but I can't learn while you and Miss Murdstone are by. I can't indeed!"

"Can't you, indeed, David?" he said. "We'll try that."

He had my head as in a vice, but I twined round him somehow, and stopped him for a moment, entreating him not to beat me. It was only a moment that I stopped him, for he cut me heavily an instant afterwards, and in the same instant I caught the hand with which he held me in my mouth, between my teeth, and bit it through. It sets my teeth on edge to think of it.

He beat me then, as if he would have beaten me to death. Above all the noise we made, I heard them running up the stairs, and crying out – I heard my mother crying out – and Peggotty. Then he was gone; and the door was locked outside; and I was lying, fevered and hot, and torn, and sore, and raging in my puny way, upon the floor.

How well I recollect, when I became quiet, what an unnatural stillness seemed to reign through the whole house! How well I remember, when my smart and passion began to cool, how wicked I began to feel!

I sat listening for a long while, but there was not a sound. I crawled up from the floor, and saw my face in the glass, so swollen, red, and ugly that it almost frightened me. My stripes were sore and stiff, and made me cry afresh, when I moved; but they were nothing to the guilt I felt. It lay heavier on my breast than if I had been a most atrocious criminal, I dare say.

It had begun to grow dark, and I had shut the window (I had been lying, for the most part, with my head upon the sill, by turns crying, dozing, and looking listlessly out), when the key was turned, and Miss Murdstone came in with some bread and meat, and milk. These she put down upon the table without a word, glaring at me the while with exemplary firmness, and then retired, locking the door after her.

Long after it was dark I sat there, wondering whether anybody else would come. When this appeared improbable for that night, I undressed, and went to bed; and, there, I began to wonder fearfully what would be done to me. Whether it was a criminal act that I had committed? Whether I should be taken into custody, and sent to prison? Whether I was at all in danger of being hanged?

David Copperfield, *Chapter 4*

David meets a waiter

David Copperfield has been sent away to school by his stepfather, Mr. Murdstone, and one of the indignities he has to suffer on his journey is not being recognised by his proper name: at the inn he has to answer to "Murdstone".

THE COACH was in the yard, shining very much all over, but without any horses to it as yet; and it looked in that state as if nothing was more unlikely than its ever going to London. I was thinking this, and wondering what would ultimately become of my box, which Mr. Barkis had put down on the yard-pavement by the pole (he having driven up the yard to turn his cart), and also what would ultimately become of me, when a lady looked out of a bow-window where some fowls and joints of meat were hanging up, and said:

"Is that the little gentleman from Blunderstone?"

"Yes, ma'am," I said.

"What name?" inquired the lady.

"Copperfield, ma'am," I said.

"That won't do," returned the lady. "Nobody's dinner is paid for here, in that name."

"Is it Murdstone, ma'am?" I said.

"If you're Master Murdstone," said the lady, "why do you go and give another name, first?"

I explained to the lady how it was, who then rang a bell, and called out, "William! show the coffee-room!" upon which a waiter came running out of a kitchen on the opposite side of the yard to show it, and seemed a good deal surprised when he was only to show it to me.

It was a large long room with some large maps in it. I doubt if I could have felt much stranger if the maps had been real foreign countries, and I cast away in the middle of them. I felt it was taking a liberty to sit down, with my cap in my hand, on the corner of the chair nearest the door; and when the waiter laid a cloth on purpose for me, and put a set of casters on it, I think I must have turned red all over with modesty.

He brought me some chops, and vegetables, and took the covers off in such a bouncing manner that I was afraid I must have given him some offence. But he greatly relieved my mind by putting a chair for me at the table, and saying, very affably, "Now, six-foot! come on!"

"There's half a pint of ale for you."

I thanked him, and took my seat at the board; but found it extremely difficult to handle my knife and fork with anything like dexterity, or to avoid splashing myself with the gravy, while he was standing opposite, staring so hard, and making me blush in the most dreadful manner every time I caught his eye. After watching me into the second chop, he said:

"There's half a pint of ale for you. Will you have it now?"

I thanked him and said, "Yes." Upon which he poured it out of a jug into a large tumbler, and held it up against the light, and made it look beautiful.

"My eye!" he said. "It seems a good deal, don't it?"

"It does seem a good deal," I answered with a smile. For it was quite delightful to me, to find him so pleasant. He was a twinkling-eyed, pimple-faced man, with his hair standing upright all over his head; and as he stood with one arm a-kimbo, holding up the glass to the light with the other hand, he looked quite friendly.

"There was a gentleman here, yesterday," he said – "a stout gentleman, by the name of Topsawyer – perhaps you know him?"

"No," I said, "I don't think – "

"In breeches and gaiters, broad-brimmed hat, grey coat, speckled choker," said the waiter.

"No," I said bashfully, "I haven't the pleasure – "

"He came in here," said the waiter, looking at the light through the tumbler, "ordered a glass of this ale – *would* order it – I told him not – drank it, and fell dead. It was too old for him. It oughtn't to be drawn; that's the fact."

I was very much shocked to hear of this melancholy accident, and said I thought I had better have some water.

"Why you see," said the waiter, still looking at the light through the tumbler, with one of his eyes shut up, "our people don't like things being ordered and left. It offends 'em. But *I*'ll drink it, if you like. I'm used to it, and use is everything. I don't think it'll hurt me, if I throw my head back, and take it off quick. Shall I?"

I replied that he would much oblige me by drinking it, if he thought he could do it safely, but by no means otherwise. When he did throw his head back, and take it off quick, I had a horrible fear, I confess, of seeing him meet the fate of the lamented Mr. Topsawyer, and fall lifeless on the carpet. But it didn't hurt him. On the contrary, I thought he seemed the fresher for it.

"What have we got here?" he said, putting a fork into my dish. "Not chops?"

"Chops," I said.

"Lord bless my soul!" he exclaimed, "I didn't know they were chops. Why, a chop's the very thing to take off the bad effects of that beer! Ain't it lucky?"

So he took a chop by the bone in one hand, and a potato in the other, and ate away with a very good appetite, to my extreme satisfaction. He afterwards took another chop, and another potato; and after that, another chop and another potato. When we had done, he brought me a pudding, and having set it before me, seemed to ruminate, and to become absent in his mind for some moments.

"How's the pie?" he said, rousing himself.

"It's a pudding," I made answer.

"Pudding!" he exclaimed. "Why, bless me, so it is! What!" looking at it nearer. "You don't mean to say it's a batter-pudding!"

"Yes, it is indeed."

"Why, a batter-pudding," he said, taking up a tablespoon, "is my favourite pudding! Ain't that lucky? Come on, little 'un, and let's see who'll get most."

The waiter certainly got most. He entreated me more than once to come in and win, but what with his tablespoon to my teaspoon, his dispatch to my dispatch, and his appetite to my appetite, I was left far behind at the first mouthful, and had no chance with him. I never saw anyone enjoy a pudding so much, I think; and he laughed, when it was all gone, as if his enjoyment of it lasted still.

Finding him so very friendly and companionable, it was then that I asked for the pen and ink and paper, to write to Peggotty. He not only brought it immediately, but was good enough to look over me while I wrote the letter. When I had finished it, he asked me where I was going to school.

I said, "Near London," which was all I knew.

"Oh! my eye!" he said, looking very low-spirited, "I am sorry for that."

"Why?" I asked him.

"Oh, Lord!" he said, shaking his head, "that's the school where they broke the boy's ribs – two ribs – a little boy he was. I should say he was – let me see – how old are you, about?"

I told him between eight and nine.

"That's just his age," he said. "He was eight years and six months old when they broke his first rib; eight years and eight months old when they broke his second, and did for him."

I could not disguise from myself, or from the waiter, that this was an uncomfortable coincidence, and inquired how it was done. His answer was not cheering to my spirits, for it consisted of two dismal words, "With whopping."

The blowing of the coach-horn in the yard was a seasonable diversion, which made me get up and hesitatingly inquire, in the mingled pride and diffidence of having a purse (which I took out of my pocket), if there were anything to pay.

"There's a sheet of letter-paper," he returned. "Did you ever buy a sheet of letter-paper?"

I could not remember that I ever had.

"It's dear," he said, "on account of the duty. Threepence. That's the way we're taxed in this country. There's nothing else, except the waiter. Never mind the ink. *I* lose by that."

"What should you – what should I – how much ought I to – what would it be right to pay the waiter, if you please?" I stammered, blushing.

"If I hadn't a family, and that family hadn't the cowpock," said the waiter, "I wouldn't take a sixpence. If I didn't support a aged pairint, and a lovely sister," – here the waiter was greatly agitated – "I wouldn't take a farthing. If I had a good place, and was treated well here, I should beg acceptance of a trifle, instead of taking of it. But I live on broken wittles – and I sleep on the coals" – here the waiter burst into tears.

I was very much concerned for his misfortunes, and felt that any recognition short of ninepence would be mere brutality and hardness of heart. Therefore I gave him one of my three bright shillings*, which he received with much humility and veneration, and spun up with his thumb, directly afterwards, to try the goodness of.

David Copperfield, *Chapter 5*

* three shillings; (old money) now equal to 15p

Dotheboys Hall

In the 1830s a cluster of Yorkshire schools attained notoriety as inhumane dumping-grounds for unwanted children, often illegitimate. Dickens visited Yorkshire to research material for this part of **Nicholas Nickleby**. *Nicholas has just been appointed as a teacher to the appropriately named Dotheboys Hall by the equally appropriately named Wackford Squeers.*

A RIDE of two hundred and odd miles in severe weather, is one of the best softeners of a hard bed that ingenuity can devise. Perhaps it is even a sweetener of dreams, for those which hovered over the rough couch of Nicholas and whispered their airy nothings in his ear, were of an agreeable and happy kind. He was making his fortune very fast indeed, when the faint glimmer of an expiring candle shone before his eyes, and a voice he had no difficulty in recognising as part and parcel of Mr. Squeers, admonished him that it was time to rise.

"Past seven, Nickleby," said Mr. Squeers.

"Has morning come already?" asked Nicholas, sitting up in bed.

"Ah! that has it," replied Squeers, "and ready iced too. Now, Nickleby, come: tumble up, will you?"

Nicholas needed no further admonition, but "tumbled up" at once, and proceeded to dress himself by the light of the taper, which Mr. Squeers carried in his hand.

"Here's a pretty go," said that gentleman; "the pump's froze."

"Indeed!" said Nicholas, not much interested in the intelligence.

"Yes," replied Squeers. "You can't wash yourself this morning."

"Not wash myself!" exclaimed Nicholas.

"No, not a bit of it," rejoined Squeers tartly. "So you must be content with giving yourself a dry polish till we break the ice in the well, and can get a bucketful out for the boys. Don't stand staring at me, but do look sharp, will you?"

Offering no further observation, Nicholas huddled on his clothes. Squeers, meanwhile, opened the shutters and blew the candle out; when the voice of his amiable consort was heard in the passage, demanding admittance.

"Come in, my love," said Squeers.

Mrs. Squeers came in, still habited in the primitive night-jacket which had displayed the symmetry of her figure on the previous night, and further ornamented with a beaver bonnet of some antiquity, which she wore, with much ease and lightness, on the top of the nightcap before mentioned.

"Drat the things," said the lady, opening the cupboard; "I can't find the school spoon anywhere."

"Never mind it, my dear," observed Squeers in a soothing manner, "it's of no consequence."

"No consequence, why how you talk!" retorted Mrs. Squeers sharply; "isn't it brimstone* morning?"

"I forgot, my dear," rejoined Squeers; "yes, it certainly is. We purify the boys' bloods now and then, Nickleby."

"Purify fiddlesticks' ends," said his lady. "Don't think, young man, that we go to the expense of flower of brimstone and molasses, just to purify them; because if you think we carry on the business in that way, you'll find yourself mistaken, and so I tell you plainly."

"My dear," said Squeers frowning. "Hem!"

"Oh! nonsense," rejoined Mrs. Squeers. "If the young man comes to be a teacher here, let him understand, at once, that we don't want any foolery about the boys. They have the brimstone and treacle, partly because if they hadn't something or other in the way of medicine they'd be always ailing and giving a world of trouble, and partly because it spoils their appetites and comes cheaper than breakfast and dinner. So, it does them good and us good at the same time, and that's fair enough, I'm sure."

Having given this explanation, Mrs. Squeers put her hand into the closet and instituted a stricter search after the spoon, in which Mr. Squeers assisted. A few words passed between them while they were thus engaged, but as their voices were partially stifled by the cupboard, all that Nicholas could distinguish was, that Mr. Squeers said what Mrs. Squeers had said, was injudicious, and that Mrs. Squeers said what Mr. Squeers said, was "stuff".

A vast deal of searching and rummaging ensued, and it proving fruitless, Smike was called in, and pushed by Mrs. Squeers, and boxed by Mr. Squeers; which course of treatment brightening his intellects, enabled him to suggest that possibly Mrs. Squeers might have the spoon in her pocket, as indeed turned out to be the case. As Mrs. Squeers had previously protested, however, that she was quite certain she had not got it, Smike received another box on the ear for presuming to contradict his mistress, together with a promise of a sound thrashing if he were not more respectful in future; so that he took nothing very advantageous by his motion.

* brimstone: sulphur. Treacle was added to make it swallowable. It was intended as a purgative but was probably equally effective at sapping the morale of rebellious boarders as well as spoiling their appetite and thereby saving money.

"A most invaluable woman, that, Nickleby," said Squeers when his consort had hurried away, pushing the drudge before her.

"Indeed, sir!" observed Nicholas.

"I don't know her equal," said Squeers; "I do not know her equal. That woman, Nickleby, is always the same – always the same bustling, lively, active, saving creetur that you see her now."

Nicholas sighed involuntarily at the thought of the agreeable domestic prospect thus opened to him; but Squeers was, fortunately, too much occupied with his own reflections to perceive it.

"It's my way to say, when I am up in London," continued Squeers, "that to them boys she is a mother. But she is more than a mother to them; ten times more. She does things for them boys, Nickleby, that I don't believe half the mothers going, would for their own sons."

"I should think they would not, sir," answered Nicholas.

Now, the fact was, that both Mr. and Mrs. Squeers viewed the boys in the light of their proper and natural enemies; or, in other words, they held and considered that their business and profession was to get as much from every boy as could by possibility be screwed out of him. On this point they were both agreed, and behaved in unison accordingly. The only difference between them was, that Mrs. Squeers waged war against the enemy openly and fearlessly, and that Squeers covered his rascality, even at home, with a spice of his habitual deceit; as if he really had a notion of some day or other being able to take himself in, and persuade his own mind that he was a very good fellow.

"But come," said Squeers, interrupting the progress of some thoughts to this effect in the mind of his usher, "let's go to the school-room; and lend me a hand with my school coat, will you?"

Nicholas assisted his master to put on an old fustian shooting-jacket, which he took down from a peg in the passage; and Squeers, arming himself with his cane, led the way across a yard, to a door in the rear of the house.

"There," said the schoolmaster as they stepped in together; "this is our shop, Nickleby!"

It was such a crowded scene, and there were so many objects to attract attention, that, at first, Nicholas stared about him, really without seeing anything at all. By degrees, however, the place resolved itself into a bare and dirty room, with a couple of windows, whereof a tenth part might be of glass, the remainder being stopped up with old copybooks and paper. There were a couple of long old rickety desks, cut and notched, and inked, and damaged, in every possible way: two or three forms; a detached desk for Squeers; and another for his assistant. The ceiling was supported, like that of a barn, by cross beams and rafters;

and the walls were so stained and discoloured that it was impossible to tell whether they had ever been touched with paint or whitewash.

But the pupils – the young noblemen! How the last faint traces of hope, the remotest glimmering of any good to be derived from his efforts in this den, faded from the mind of Nicholas as he looked in dismay around! Pale and haggard faces, lank and bony figures, children with the countenances of old men, deformities with irons upon their limbs, boys of stunted growth, and others whose long meagre legs would hardly bear their stooping bodies, all crowded on the view together; there were the bleared eye, the hare-lip, the crooked foot, and every ugliness or distortion that told of unnatural aversion conceived by parents for their offspring, or of young lives which, from the earliest dawn of infancy, had been one horrible endurance of cruelty and neglect. There were little faces which should have been handsome, darkened with the scowl of sullen, dogged suffering; there was childhood with the light of its eye quenched, its beauty gone, and its helplessness alone remaining; there were vicious-faced boys, brooding, with leaden eyes, like malefactors in a jail; and there were young creatures on whom the sins of their frail parents had descended, weeping even for the mercenary nurses they had known, and lonesome even in their loneliness. With every kindly sympathy and affection blasted in its birth, with every young and healthy feeling flogged and starved down, with every revengeful passion that can fester in swollen hearts eating its evil way to their core in silence, what an incipient Hell was breeding here!

And yet this scene, painful as it was, had its grotesque features, which, in a less interested observer than Nicholas, might have provoked a smile. Mrs. Squeers stood at one of the desks, presiding over an immense basin of brimstone and treacle, of which delicious compound she administered a large instalment to each boy in succession: using for the purpose a common wooden spoon, which might have been originally manufactured for some gigantic top, and which widened every young gentleman's mouth considerably: they being all obliged, under heavy corporal penalties, to take in the whole of the bowl at a gasp. In another corner, huddled together for companionship, were the little boys who had arrived on the preceding night, three of them in very large leather breeches, and two in old trousers, a something tighter fit than drawers are usually worn; at no great distance from these was seated the juvenile son and heir of Mr. Squeers – a striking likeness of his father – kicking, with great vigour, under the hands of Smike, who was fitting upon him a pair of new boots that bore a most suspicious resemblance to those which the least of the little boys had worn on the journey down – as the little boy himself seemed to think, for he was regarding the appropriation with a look of most rueful amazement. Besides these, there was a long row of boys waiting, with countenances of no pleasant anticipation, to be treacled; and another file, who had just escaped from the infliction, making a variety of wry mouths indicative of anything but satisfaction. The whole were attired in such motley, ill-sorted, extraordinary garments, as would have been irresistibly ridiculous, but for the foul appearance of dirt, disorder, and disease, with which they were associated.

"Now," said Squeers, giving the desk a great rap with his cane, which made half the little boys nearly jump out of their boots, "is that physicking over?"

"Just over," said Mrs. Squeers, choking the last boy in her hurry, and tapping the crown of his head with the wooden spoon to restore him. "Here, you Smike; take away now. Look sharp!"

Smike shuffled out with the basin, and Mrs. Squeers having called up a little boy with a curly head and wiped her hands upon it, hurried out after him into a species of wash-house, where there was a small fire and a large kettle, together with a number of little wooden bowls which were arranged upon a board.

Into these bowls, Mrs. Squeers, assisted by the hungry servant, poured a brown composition which looked like diluted pincushions without the covers, and was called porridge. A minute wedge of brown bread was inserted in each bowl, and when they had eaten their porridge by means of the bread, the boys ate the bread itself, and had finished their breakfast; whereupon Mr. Squeers said, in a solemn voice, "For what we have received, may the Lord make us truly thankful!" – and went away to his own.

Nicholas distended his stomach with a bowl of porridge, for much the same reason which induces some savages to swallow earth – lest they should be inconveniently hungry when there is nothing to eat. Having further disposed of a slice of bread and butter, allotted to him in virtue of his office, he sat himself down to wait for school-time.

He could not but observe how silent and sad the boys all seemed to be. There was none of the noise and clamour of a school-room; none of its boisterous play, or hearty mirth. The children sat crouching and shivering together, and seemed to lack the spirit to move about. The only pupil who evinced the slightest tendency towards locomotion or playfulness was Master Squeers, and as his chief amusement was to tread upon the other boys' toes in his new boots, his flow of spirits was rather disagreeable than otherwise.

After some half-hour's delay, Mr. Squeers reappeared, and the boys took their places and their books, of which latter commodity the average might be about one to eight learners. A few minutes having elapsed, during which Mr. Squeers looked very profound, as if he had a perfect apprehension of what was inside all the books, and could say every word of their contents by heart if he only chose to take the trouble, that gentleman called up the first class.

Obedient to this summons there ranged themselves in front of the schoolmaster's desk, half-a-dozen scarecrows, out at knees and elbows, one of whom placed a torn and filthy book beneath his learned eye.

"This is the first class in English spelling and philosophy, Nickleby," said Squeers, beckoning Nicholas to stand beside him. "We'll get up a Latin one, and hand that over to you. Now, then, where's the first boy?"

"Please, sir, he's cleaning the back parlour window," said the temporary head of the philosophical class.

"So he is, to be sure," rejoined Squeers. "We go upon the practical mode of teaching, Nickleby; the regular education system. C-l-e-a-n, clean, verb active, to make bright, to scour. W-i-n, win, d-e-r-, der, winder, a casement. When the boy knows this out of the book, he goes and does it. It's just the same principle as the use of the globes. Where's the second boy?"

"Please, sir, he's weeding the garden," replied a small voice.

"To be sure," said Squeers, by no means disconcerted. "So he is. B-o-t, bot, t-i-n-, tin, bottin, n-e-y, ney, bottinney, noun substantive, a knowledge of plants. When he has learned that bottinney means a knowledge of plants, he goes and knows 'em. That's our system, Nickleby; what do you think of it?"

"It's a very useful one, at any rate," answered Nicholas.

"I believe you," rejoined Squeers, not remarking the emphasis of his usher. "Third boy, what's a horse?"

"A beast, sir," replied the boy.

"So it is," said Squeers. "Ain't it, Nickleby?"

"I believe there is no doubt of that, sir," answered Nicholas.

"Of course there isn't," said Squeers. "A horse is a quadruped, and quadruped's Latin for beast, as every body that's gone through the grammar, knows, or else where's the use of having grammars at all?"

"Where, indeed!" said Nicholas abstractedly.

"As you're perfect in that," resumed Squeers, turning to the boy, "go and look after *my* horse, and rub him down well, or I'll rub you down. The rest of the class go and draw water up, till somebody tells you to leave off, for it's washing-day tomorrow, and they want the coppers filled."

So saying, he dismissed the first class to their experiments in practical philosophy, and eyed Nicholas with a look, half cunning and half doubtful, as if he were not altogether certain what he might think of him by this time.

"That's the way we do it, Nickleby," he said, after a pause.

Nicholas shrugged his shoulders in a manner that was scarcely perceptible, and said he saw it was.

"And a very good way it is, too," said Squeers. "Now, just take them fourteen little boys and hear them some reading, because, you know, you must begin to be useful. Idling about here, won't do."

Mr. Squeers said this, as if it had suddenly occurred to him, either that he must not say too much to his assistant, or that his assistant did not say enough to him in praise of the establishment. The children were arranged in a semicircle round the new master, and he was soon listening to their dull, drawling, hesitating recital of those stories of engrossing interest which are to be found in the more antiquated spelling books.

In this exciting occupation, the morning lagged heavily on. At one o'clock, the boys, having previously had their appetites thoroughly taken away by stir-about* and potatoes, sat down in the kitchen to some hard salt beef, of which Nicholas was graciously permitted to take his portion to his own solitary desk, to eat it there in peace. After this, there was another hour of crouching in the school-room and shivering with cold, and then school began again.

It was Mr. Squeers's custom to call the boys together and make a sort of report, after every half-yearly visit to the metropolis, regarding the relations and friends he had seen, the news he had heard, the letters he had brought down, the bills which had been paid, the accounts which had been left unpaid, and so forth. This solemn proceeding always took place in the afternoon of the day succeeding his return; perhaps, because the boys acquired strength of mind from the suspense of the morning, or, possibly, because Mr. Squeers himself acquired greater sternness and inflexibility from certain warm potations in which he was wont to indulge after his early dinner. Be this as it may, the boys were recalled from house-window, garden, stable, and cow-yard, and the school were assembled in full conclave, when Mr. Squeers, with a small bundle of papers in his hand, and Mrs. S. following with a pair of canes, entered the room and proclaimed silence.

"Let any boy speak a word without leave," said Mr. Squeers mildly, "and I'll take the skin off his back."

This special proclamation had the desired effect, and a death-like silence immediately prevailed, in the midst of which Mr. Squeers went on to say:

"Boys, I've been to London, and have returned to my family and you, as strong and well as ever."

According to half-yearly custom, the boys gave three feeble cheers at this refreshing intelligence. Such cheers! Sighs of extra strength with the chill on.

* stir-about: porridge

"I have seen the parents of some boys," continued Squeers, turning over his papers, "and they're so glad to hear how their sons are getting on, that there's no prospect at all of their going away, which of course is a very pleasant thing to reflect upon, for all parties."

Two or three hands went to two or three eyes when Squeers said this, but the greater part of the young gentlemen having no particular parents to speak of, were wholly uninterested in the thing one way or other.

"I have had disappointments to contend against," said Squeers, looking very grim; "Bolder's father was two pound ten short. Where is Bolder?"

"Here he is, please sir," rejoined twenty officious voices. Boys are very like men to be sure.

"Come here, Bolder," said Squeers.

An unhealthy-looking boy, with warts all over his hands, stepped from his place to the master's desk, and raised his eyes imploringly to Squeers's face; his own, quite white from the rapid beating of his heart.

"Bolder," said Squeers, speaking very slowly, for he was considering, as the saying goes, where to have him. "Bolder, if your father thinks that because – why, what's this, sir?"

As Squeers spoke, he caught up the boy's hand by the cuff of his jacket, and surveyed it with an edifying aspect of horror and disgust.

"What do you call this, sir?" demanded the schoolmaster, administering a cut with the cane to expedite the reply.

"I can't help it, indeed, sir," rejoined the boy, crying. "They will come; it's the dirty work I think, sir – at least I don't know what it is, sir, but it's not my fault."

"Bolder," said Squeers, tucking up his wristbands, and moistening the palm of his right hand to get a good grip of the cane, "you are an incorrigible young scoundrel, and as the last thrashing did you no good, we must see what another will do towards beating it out of you."

With this, and wholly disregarding a piteous cry for mercy, Mr. Squeers fell upon the boy and caned him soundly; not leaving off indeed, until his arm was tired out.

Nicholas Nickleby, *Chapter 8*

"Fact, fact, fact!"

*The chapter of **Hard Times** from which this extract comes is called 'Murdering the innocents'. In it Dickens presents Thomas Gradgrind, a schoolmaster and disciple of Benthamism (or Utilitarianism), a doctrine that stressed the need to judge actions by their usefulness, practicality, and the advancement of happiness of the greatest number, seemingly at the expense of the individual and of the life of the imagination.*

THOMAS GRADGRIND, sir. A man of realities. A man of facts and calculations. A man who proceeds upon the principle that two and two are four, and nothing over, and who is not to be talked into allowing for anything over. Thomas Gradgrind, sir – peremptorily Thomas – Thomas Gradgrind. With a rule and a pair of scales, and the multiplication table always in his pocket, sir, ready to weigh and measure any parcel of human nature, and tell you exactly what it comes to. It is a mere question of figures, a case of simple arithmetic. You might hope to get some other nonsensical belief into the head of George Gradgrind, or Augustus Gradgrind, or John Gradgrind, or Joseph Gradgrind (all suppositious, non-existent persons), but into the head of Thomas Gradgrind – no, sir!

In such terms Mr. Gradgrind always mentally introduced himself, whether to his private circle of acquaintance, or to the public in general. In such terms, no doubt, substituting the words "boys and girls", for "sir", Thomas Gradgrind now presented Thomas Gradgrind to the little pitchers before him, who were to be filled so full of facts.

Indeed, as he eagerly sparkled at them from the cellarage before mentioned, he seemed a kind of cannon loaded to the muzzle with facts, and prepared to blow them clean out of the regions of childhood at one discharge. He seemed a galvanising apparatus, too, charged with a grim mechanical substitute for the tender young imaginations that were to be stormed away.

"Girl number twenty," said Mr. Gradgrind, squarely pointing with his square forefinger, "I don't know that girl. Who is that girl?"

"Sissy Jupe, sir," explained number twenty, blushing, standing up, and curtseying.

"Sissy is not a name," said Mr. Gradgrind. "Don't call yourself Sissy. Call yourself Cecilia."

"It's father as calls me Sissy, sir," returned the young girl in a trembling voice, and with another curtsey.

"Then he has no business to do it," said Mr. Gradgrind. "Tell him he mustn't. Cecilia Jupe. Let me see. What is your father?"

"He belongs to the horse-riding,* if you please, sir."

Mr. Gradgrind frowned, and waved off the objectionable calling with his hand.

"We don't want to know anything about that, here. You mustn't tell us about that, here. Your father breaks horses, don't he?"

"If you please, sir, when they can get any to break, they do break horses in the ring, sir."

"You mustn't tell us about the ring, here. Very well, then. Describe your father as a horsebreaker. He doctors sick horses, I dare say?"

"Oh yes, sir."

"Very well, then. He is a veterinary surgeon, a farrier and horsebreaker. Give me your definition of a horse."

(Sissy Jupe thrown into the greatest alarm by this demand.)

"Girl number twenty unable to define a horse!" said Mr. Gradgrind, for the general behoof of all the little pitchers. "Girl number twenty possessed of no facts, in reference to one of the commonest of animals! Some boy's definition of a horse. Bitzer, yours."

The square finger, moving here and there, lighted suddenly on Bitzer, perhaps because he chanced to sit in the same ray of sunlight which, darting in at one of the bare windows of the intensely whitewashed room, irradiated Sissy. For, the boys and girls sat on the face of the inclined plane in two compact bodies, divided up the centre by a narrow interval; and Sissy, being at the corner of a row on the sunny side, came in for the beginning of a sunbeam, of which Bitzer, being at the corner of a row on the other side, a few rows in advance, caught the end. But, whereas the girl was so dark-eyed and dark-haired, that she seemed to receive a deeper and more lustrous colour from the sun when it shone upon her, the boy was so light-eyed and light-haired that the self-same rays appeared to draw out of him what little colour he ever possessed. His cold eyes would hardly have been eyes, but for the short ends of lashes which, by bringing them into immediate contrast with something paler than themselves, expressed their form. His short-cropped hair might have been a mere continuation of the sandy freckles on his forehead and face. His skin was so unwholesomely deficient in the natural tinge, that he looked as though, if he were cut, he would bleed white.

"Bitzer," said Thomas Gradgrind. "Your definition of a horse."

* horse-riding: Sissy's father is a circus owner.

"Quadruped. Graminivorous. Forty teeth, namely twenty-four grinders, four eye-teeth, and twelve incisive. Sheds coat in the spring; in marshy countries, sheds hoofs, too. Hoofs hard, but requiring to be shod with iron. Age known by marks in mouth." Thus (and much more) Bitzer.

"Now girl number twenty," said Mr. Gradgrind. "You know what a horse is."

She curtseyed again, and would have blushed deeper, if she could have blushed deeper than she had blushed all this time. Bitzer, after rapidly blinking at Thomas Gradgrind with both eyes at once, and so catching the light upon his quivering ends of lashes that they looked like the antennae of busy insects, put his knuckles to his freckled forehead, and sat down again.

The third gentleman now stepped forth. A mighty man at cutting and drying, he was; a government officer; in his way (and in most other people's too), a professed pugilist; always in training, always with a system to force down the general throat like a bolus*, always to be heard of at the bar of his little Public-office, ready to fight all England. To continue in fistic phraseology, he had a genius for coming up to the scratch, wherever and whatever it was, and proving himself an ugly customer. He would go in and damage any subject whatever with his right, follow up with his left, stop, exchange, counter, bore his opponent (he always fought All England*) to the ropes, and fall upon him neatly. He was certain to knock the wind out of common sense, and render that unlucky adversary deaf to the call of time. And he had it in charge from high authority to bring about the great public-office Millennium, when Commissioners should reign upon earth.

"Very well," said this gentleman, briskly smiling, and folding his arms. "That's a horse. Now, let me ask you girls and boys, Would you paper a room with representations of horses?"

After a pause, one half of the children cried in chorus, "Yes, sir!" Upon which the other half, seeing in the gentleman's face that Yes was wrong, cried out in chorus, "No, sir!" – as the custom is, in these examinations.

"Of course, No. Why wouldn't you?"

A pause. One corpulent slow boy, with a wheezy manner of breathing, ventured the answer, Because he wouldn't paper a room at all, but would paint it.

"You *must* paper it," said the gentleman, rather warmly.

"You must paper it," said Thomas Gradgrind, "whether you like it or not. Don't tell *us* you wouldn't paper it. What do you mean, boy?"

* bolus: a large pill.

* All England: the code governing prize-fighting, before the Queensberry Rules of 1867.

"I'll explain to you, then," said the gentleman, after another and a dismal pause, "why you wouldn't paper a room with representations of horses. Do you ever see horses walking up and down the sides of rooms in reality – in fact? Do you?"

"Yes, sir!" from one half. "No, sir!" from the other.

"Of course no," said the gentleman, with an indignant look at the wrong half. "Why, then, you are not to see anywhere, what you don't see in fact; you are not to have anywhere, what you don't have in fact. What is called Taste, is only another name for Fact."

Thomas Gradgrind nodded his approbation.

"This is a new principle, a discovery, a great discovery," said the gentleman. "Now, I'll try you again. Suppose you were going to carpet a room. Would you use a carpet having a representation of flowers upon it?"

There being a general conviction by this time that "No, sir!" was always the right answer to this gentleman, the chorus of No was very strong. Only a few feeble stragglers said Yes: among them Sissy Jupe.

"Girl number twenty," said the gentleman, smiling in the calm strength of knowledge.

Sissy blushed, and stood up.

"So you would carpet your room – or your husband's room, if you were a grown woman, and had a husband – with representations of flowers, would you?" said the gentleman. "Why would you?"

"If you please, sir, I am very fond of flowers," returned the girl.

"And is that why you would put tables and chairs upon them, and have people walking over them with heavy boots?"

"It wouldn't hurt them, sir. They wouldn't crush and wither, if you please, sir. They would be the pictures of what was very pretty and pleasant, and I would fancy – "

"Ay, ay, ay! But you mustn't fancy," cried the gentleman, quite elated by coming so happily to his point. "That's it! You are never to fancy."

"You are not, Cecilia Jupe," Thomas Gradgrind solemnly repeated, "to do anything of that kind."

"Fact, fact, fact!" said the gentleman. And "Fact, fact, fact!" repeated Thomas Gradgrind.

Hard Times, *Chapter 2*

The new boy

There are very few good schools in Dickens's novels and Salem House where David Copperfield is sent as a boarder is not one of them. David, when being brutally thrashed, had bitten the hand of his stepfather (see page 18) whose malevolence reaches out even here and is compounded by the cruelty of the headmaster, Mr. Creakle.

Mr. Mell is a kindly assistant master who takes David under his wing as far as he can.

A SHORT walk brought us – I mean the Master and me – to Salem House, which was enclosed with a high brick wall, and looked very dull. Over a door in this wall was a board with SALEM HOUSE upon it; and through a grating in this door we were surveyed when we rang the bell by a surly face, which I found, on the door being opened, belonged to a stout man with a bull-neck, a wooden leg, overhanging temples, and his hair cut close all round his head.

"The new boy," said the Master.

The man with the wooden leg eyed me all over – it didn't take long, for there was not much of me – and locked the gate behind us, and took out the key. We were going up to the house, among some dark heavy trees, when he called after my conductor.

"Hallo!"

We looked back, and he was standing at the door of a little lodge, where he lived, with a pair of boots in his hand.

"Here! The cobbler's been," he said, "since you've been out, Mr. Mell, and he says he can't mend 'em any more. He says there ain't a bit of the original boot left, and he wonders you expect it."

With these words he threw the boots towards Mr. Mell, who went back a few paces to pick them up, and looked at them (very disconsolately, I was afraid), as we went on together. I observed then, for the first time, that the boots he had on were a good deal the worse for wear, and that his stocking was just breaking out in one place, like a bud.

Salem House was a square brick building with wings; of a bare and unfurnished appearance. All about it was so very quiet, that I said to Mr. Mell I supposed the boys were out; but he seemed surprised at my not knowing that it was holiday-time. That all the boys were at their several homes. That Mr. Creakle, the proprietor, was down by the sea-side with Mrs. and Miss Creakle; and that I was sent in holiday-time as a punishment for my misdoing. All of which he explained to me as we went along.

I gazed upon the schoolroom into which he took me, as the most forlorn and desolate place I had ever seen. I see it now. A long room with three long rows of desks, and six of forms, and bristling all round with pegs for hats and slates. Scraps of old copy-books and exercises litter the dirty floor. Some silkworms' houses, made of the same materials, are scattered over the desks. Two miserable little white mice, left behind by their owner, are running up and down in a fusty castle made of paste-board and wire, looking in all the corners with their red eyes for any-thing to eat. A bird, in a cage very little bigger than himself, makes a mournful rattle now and then in hopping on his perch, two inches high, or dropping from it; but neither sings nor chirps. There is a strange unwholesome smell upon the room, like mildewed corduroys, sweet apples wanting air, and rotten books. There could not well be more ink splashed about it, if it had been roofless from its first construction, and the skies had rained, snowed, hailed, and blown ink through the varying seasons of the year.

Mr. Mell having left me while he took his irreparable boots upstairs, I went softly to the upper end of the room, observing all this as I crept along. Suddenly I came upon a pasteboard placard, beautifully written, which was lying on the desk, and bore these words: "*Take care of him. He bites.*"

I got upon the desk immediately, apprehensive of at least a great dog underneath. But, though I looked all round with anxious eyes, I could see nothing of him. I was still engaged in peering about, when Mr. Mell came back, and asked me what I did up there?

"I beg your pardon, sir," says I, "if you please, I'm looking for the dog."

"Dog?" he says. "What dog?"

"Isn't it a dog, sir?"

"Isn't what a dog?"

"That's to be taken care of, sir; that bites."

"No, Copperfield," says he, gravely, "that's not a dog. That's a boy. My instructions are, Copperfield, to put this placard on your back. I am sorry to make such a beginning with you, but I must do it."

With that he took me down, and tied the placard, which was neatly constructed for the purpose, on my shoulders like a knapsack; and wherever I went, afterwards, I had the consolation of carrying it.

What I suffered from that placard, nobody can imagine. Whether it was possible for people to see me or not, I always fancied that somebody was reading it. It was no relief to turn round and find nobody; for wherever my back was, there I imagined somebody always to be. That cruel man with the wooden leg aggravated my sufferings. He was in authority; and if he ever saw me leaning against a tree, or a wall, or the house, he roared out from his lodge door in a stupendous voice, "Hallo, you sir! You Copperfield! Show that badge conspicuous, or I'll report you!" The playground was a bare gravelled yard, open to all the back of the house and the offices; and I knew that the servants read it, and the butcher read it, and the baker read it; that everybody, in a word, who came backwards and forwards to the house, of a morning when I was ordered to walk there, read that I was to be taken care of, for I bit. I recollect that I positively began to have a dread of myself, as a kind of wild boy who did bite.

There was an old door in this playground, on which the boys had a custom of carving their names. It was completely covered with such inscriptions. In my dread of the end of the vacation and their coming back, I could not read a boy's name, without inquiring in what tone and with what emphasis *he* would read, "Take care of him. He bites." There was one boy – a certain J. Steerforth – who cut his name very deep and very often, who, I conceived, would read it in a rather strong voice, and afterwards pull my hair. There was another boy, one Tommy Traddles, who I dreaded would make game of it, and pretend to be dreadfully frightened of me. There was a third, George Demple, who I fancied would sing it. I have looked, a little shrinking creature, at that door, until the owners of all the names – there were five-and-forty of them in the school then, Mr. Mell said – seemed to send me to Coventry by general acclamation, and to cry out, each in his own way, "Take care of him. He bites!"

David Copperfield, *Chapter 5*

Satis House

Pip, accompanied by Mr. Pumblechook, a pompous and bullying corn chandler connected with Pip's family, is sent to play at Miss Havisham's house. She is an eccentric recluse, jilted in love and obsessive about revenging herself on men through her beautiful adopted daughter, Estella, whom she educates to be an icy tormentor. Pip falls in love with her.

Mr. Pumblechook and I breakfasted at eight o'clock in the parlour behind the shop, while the shopman took his mug of tea and hunch of bread-and-butter on a sack of peas in the front premises. I considered Mr. Pumblechook wretched company. Besides being possessed by my sister's idea that a mortifying and penitential character ought to be imparted to my diet – besides giving me as much crumb as possible in combination with as little butter, and putting such a quantity of warm water into my milk that it would have been more candid to have left the milk out altogether – his conversation consisted of nothing but arithmetic. On my politely bidding him Good morning, he said, pompously, "Seven times nine, boy?" And how should *I* be able to answer, dodged in that way, in a strange place, on an empty stomach! I was hungry, but before I had swallowed a morsel, he began a running sum that lasted all through the breakfast. "Seven?" "And four?" "And eight?" "And six?" "And two?" "And ten?" And so on. And after each figure was disposed of, it was as much as I could do to get a bite or a sup, before the next came; while he sat at his ease guessing nothing, and eating bacon and hot roll, in (if I may be allowed the expression) a gorging and gormandising manner.

For such reasons I was very glad when ten o'clock came and we started for Miss Havisham's; though I was not at all at my ease regarding the manner in which I should acquit myself under that lady's roof. Within a quarter of an hour we came to Miss Havisham's house, which was of old brick, and dismal, and had a great many iron bars to it. Some of the windows had been walled up; of those that remained, all the lower were rustily barred. There was a court-yard in front, and that was barred; so, we had to wait, after ringing the bell, until some one should come to open it. While we waited at the gate, I peeped in (even then Mr. Pumblechook said, "And fourteen?" but I pretended not to hear him), and saw that at the side of the house there was a large brewery. No brewing was going on in it, and none seemed to have gone on for a long long time.

A window was raised, and a clear voice demanded "What name?" To which my conductor replied, "Pumblechook." The voice returned, "Quite right," and the window was shut again, and a young lady came across the court-yard, with keys in her hand.

"This," said Mr. Pumblechook, "is Pip."

"This is Pip, is it?" returned the young lady, who was very pretty and seemed very proud; "come in, Pip."

Mr. Pumblechook was coming in also, when she stopped him with the gate.

"Oh!" she said. "Did you wish to see Miss Havisham?"

"If Miss Havisham wished to see me," returned Mr. Pumblechook, discomfited.

"Ah!" said the girl; "but you see she don't."

She said it so finally, and in such an undiscussible way, that Mr. Pumblechook, though in a condition of ruffled dignity, could not protest. But he eyed me severely – as if *I* had done anything to him! – and departed with the words reproachfully delivered: "Boy! Let your behaviour here be a credit unto them which brought you up by hand!" I was not free from apprehension that he would come back to propound through the gate, "And sixteen?" But he didn't.

My young conductress locked the gate, and we went across the court-yard. It was paved and clean, but grass was growing in every crevice. The brewery buildings had a little lane of communication with it; and the wooden gates of that lane stood open, and all the brewery beyond, stood open, away to the high enclosing wall; and all was empty and disused. The cold wind seemed to blow colder there, than outside the gate; and it made a shrill noise in howling in and out at the open sides of the brewery, like the noise of wind in the rigging of a ship at sea.

She saw me looking at it, and she said, "You could drink without hurt all the strong beer that's brewed there now, boy."

"I should think I could, miss," said I, in a shy way.

"Better not try to brew beer there now, or it would turn out sour, boy; don't you think so?"

"It looks like it, miss."

"Not that anybody means to try," she added, "for that's all done with, and the place will stand as idle as it is, till it falls. As to strong beer, there's enough of it in the cellars already, to drown the Manor House."

"Is that the name of this house, miss?"

"One of its names, boy."

"It has more than one, then, miss?"

"One more. Its other name was Satis; which is Greek, or Latin, or Hebrew, or all three – or all one to me – for enough."

"Enough House," said I; "that's a curious name, miss."

"Yes," she replied; "but it meant more than it said. It meant, when it was given, that whoever had this house, could want nothing else. They must have been easily satisfied in those days, I should think. But don't loiter, boy."

Though she called me "boy" so often, and with a carelessness that was far from complimentary, she was of about my own age. She seemed much older than I, of course, being a girl, and beautiful and self-possessed; and she was as scornful of me as if she had been one-and-twenty, and a queen.

We went into the house by a side door – the great front entrance had two chains across it outside – and the first thing I noticed was, that the passages were all dark, and that she had left a candle burning there. She took it up, and we went through more passages and up a staircase, and still it was all dark, and only the candle lighted us.

At last we came to the door of a room, and she said, "Go in."

I answered, more in shyness than politeness, "After you, miss."

To this, she returned: "Don't be ridiculous, boy; I am not going in." And scornfully walked away, and – what was worse – took the candle with her.

This was very uncomfortable, and I was half afraid. However, the only thing to be done being to knock at the door, I knocked, and was told from within to enter. I entered, therefore, and found myself in a pretty large room, well lighted with wax candles. No glimpse of daylight was to be seen in it. It was a dressing-room, as I supposed from the furniture, though much of it was of forms and uses then quite unknown to me. But prominent in it was a draped table with a gilded looking-glass, and that I made out at first sight to be a fine lady's dressing-table.

Whether I should have made out this object so soon, if there had been no fine lady sitting at it, I cannot say. In an armchair, with an elbow resting on the table and her head leaning on that hand, sat the strangest lady I have ever seen, or shall ever see.

She was dressed in rich materials – satins, and lace, and silks – all of white. Her shoes were white. And she had a long white veil dependent from her hair, and she had bridal flowers in her hair, but her hair was white. Some bright jewels sparkled on her neck and on her hands, and some other jewels lay sparkling on the table. Dresses, less splendid than the dress she wore, and half-packed trunks, were scattered about. She had not quite finished dressing, for she had but one shoe on – the other was on the table near her hand – her veil was but half arranged, her watch and chain were not put on, and some lace for her bosom lay with those trinkets, and with her handkerchief, and gloves, and some flowers, and a prayer-book, all confusedly heaped about the looking-glass.

It was not in the first few moments that I saw all these things, though I saw more of them in the first moments than might be supposed. But, I saw that everything within my view which ought to be white, had been white long ago, and had lost its lustre, and was faded and yellow. I saw that the bride within the bridal dress had withered like the dress, and like the flowers, and had no brightness left but the brightness of her sunken eyes. I saw that the dress had been put upon the rounded figure of a young woman, and that the figure upon which it now hung loose, had shrunk to skin and bone. Once, I had been taken to see some ghastly waxwork at the Fair, representing I know not what impossible personage lying in state. Once, I had been taken to one of our old marsh churches to see a skeleton in the ashes of a rich dress, that had been dug out of a vault under the church pavement. Now, waxwork and skeleton seemed to have dark eyes that moved and looked at me. I should have cried out, if I could.

Great Expectations, *Chapter 8*

Pip has a fight

On another visit to Satis House, Pip meets a boy who will in later life become a firm friend, Herbert Pocket. They fight for no reason at all and without even exchanging names. Estella, who watches from a window, seals Pip's infatuation with a kiss after he wins.

I STROLLED into the garden and strolled all over it. It was quite a wilderness, and there were old melon-frames and cucumber-frames in it, which seemed in their decline to have produced a spontaneous growth of weak attempts at pieces of old hats and boots, with now and then a weedy offshoot into the likeness of a battered saucepan.

When I had exhausted the garden and a greenhouse with nothing in it but a fallen-down grape-vine and some bottles, I found myself in the dismal corner upon which I had looked out of window. Never questioning for a moment that the house was now empty, I looked in at another window, and found myself, to my great surprise, exchanging a broad stare with a pale young gentleman with red eyelids and light hair.

This pale young gentleman quickly disappeared, and re-appeared beside me. He had been at his books when I had found myself staring at him, and I now saw that he was inky.

"Halloa!" said he, "young fellow!"

Halloa being a general observation which I had usually observed to be best answered by itself, *I* said, "Halloa!" politely omitting young fellow.

"Who let *you* in?" said he.

"Miss Estella."

"Who gave you leave to prowl about?"

"Miss Estella."

"Come and fight," said the pale young gentleman.

What could I do but follow him? I have often asked myself the question since: but, what else could I do? His manner was so final and I was so astonished, that I followed where he led, as if I had been under a spell.

"Stop a minute, though," he said, wheeling round before we had gone many paces. "I ought to give you a reason for fighting, too. There it is!" In a most irritating manner he instantly slapped his hands against one another, daintily flung one of his legs up behind him, pulled my hair, slapped his hands again, dipped his head, and butted it into my stomach.

The bull-like proceeding last mentioned, besides that it was unquestionably to be regarded in the light of a liberty, was particularly disagreeable just after bread and meat. I therefore hit out at him and was going to hit out again, when he said, "Aha! Would you?" and began dancing backwards and forwards in a manner quite unparalleled within my limited experience.

"Laws of the game!" said he. Here, he skipped from his left leg on to his right. "Regular rules!" Here, he skipped from his right leg on to his left. "Come to the ground, and go through the preliminaries!" Here, he dodged backwards and forwards, and did all sorts of things while I looked helplessly at him.

I was secretly afraid of him when I saw him so dexterous; but, I felt morally and physically convinced that his light head of hair could have had no business in the pit of my stomach, and that I had a right to consider it irrelevant when so obtruded on my attention. Therefore, I followed him without a word, to a retired nook of the garden, formed by the junction of two walls and screened by some rubbish. On his asking me if I was satisfied with the ground, and on my replying Yes, he begged my leave to absent himself for a moment, and quickly returned with a bottle of water and a sponge dipped in vinegar.* "Available for both," he said, placing these against the wall. And then fell to pulling off, not only his jacket and waistcoat, but his shirt too, in a manner at once light-hearted, businesslike, and bloodthirsty.

Although he did not look very healthy – having pimples on his face, and a breaking out at his mouth – these dreadful preparations quite appalled me. I judged him to be about my own age, but he was much taller, and he had a way of spinning himself about that was full of appearance. For the rest, he was a young gentleman in a grey suit (when not denuded for battle), with his elbows, knees, wrists, and heels, considerably in advance of the rest of him as to development.

My heart failed me when I saw him squaring at me with every demonstration of mechanical nicety, and eyeing my anatomy as if he were minutely choosing his bone. I never have been so surprised in my life, as I was when I let out the first blow, and saw him lying on his back, looking up at me with a bloody nose and his face exceedingly fore-shortened.

But, he was on his feet directly, and after sponging himself with a great show of dexterity began squaring again. The second greatest sur-

* sponge dipped in vinegar: to be used like smelling salts in case either of them was knocked out or as an antiseptic for cuts.

prise I have ever had in my life was seeing him on his back again, looking up at me out of a black eye.

His spirit inspired me with great respect. He seemed to have no strength, and he never once hit me hard, and he was always knocked down; but, he would be up again in a moment, sponging himself or drinking out of the water-bottle, with the greatest satisfaction in seconding himself according to form, and then came at me with an air and a show that made me believe he really was going to do for me at last. He got heavily bruised, for I am sorry to record that the more I hit him, the harder I hit him; but, he came up again and again and again, until at last he got a bad fall with the back of his head against the wall. Even after that crisis in our affairs, he got up and turned round and round confusedly, a few times, not knowing where I was; but finally went on his knees to his sponge and threw it up: at the same time panting out, "That means you have won."

He seemed so brave and innocent, that although I had not proposed the contest I felt but a gloomy satisfaction in my victory. Indeed, I go so far as to hope that I regarded myself while dressing, as a species of savage young wolf, or other wild beast. However, I got dressed, darkly wiping my sanguinary face at intervals, and I said, "Can I help you?" and he said "No thankee," and I said "Good afternoon," and *he* said "Same to you."

When I got into the court-yard, I found Estella waiting with the keys. But, she neither asked me where I had been, nor why I had kept her waiting; and there was a bright flush upon her face, as though something had happened to delight her. Instead of going straight to the gate, too, she stepped back into the passage, and beckoned me.

"Come here! You may kiss me, if you like."

I kissed her cheek as she turned it to me. I think I would have gone through a great deal to kiss her cheek. But, I felt that the kiss was given to the coarse common boy as a piece of money might have been, and that it was worth nothing.

Great Expectations, *Chapter 11*

Maggy

Amy Dorrit was born in the Marshalsea debtors' prison in London where her father gradually succumbs to the "prison rot" and begins to enjoy his status as a senior inhabitant. Amy Dorrit, not herself a prisoner though she lives in the jail, helps support her family by needlework at the house where Clennam's mother lives. Arthur Clennam is in early middle-age but emotionally immature. He takes an interest in Amy, the Little Dorrit of the book's title, but sees her only as a child (she is twenty years old at this point). Clennam is escorting her "home" when they meet Maggy.

"As I TAKE you back – you are going back?"
"Oh yes! going straight home."

"As I take you back," the word home jarred upon him, "let me ask you to persuade yourself that you have another friend. I make no professions, and say no more."

"You are truly kind to me, sir. I am sure I need no more."

They walked back through the miserable muddy streets, and among the poor, mean shops, and were jostled by the crowds of dirty hucksters usual to a poor neighbourhood. There was nothing, by the short way, that was pleasant to any of the five senses. Yet it was not a common passage through common rain, and mire, and noise, to Clennam, having this little, slender, careful creature on his arm. How young she seemed to him, or how old he to her; or what a secret either to the other, in that beginning of the destined interweaving of their stories, matters not here. He thought of her having been born and bred among these scenes, and shrinking through them now, familiar yet misplaced; he thought of her long acquaintance with the squalid needs of life, and of her innocence; of her old solicitude for others, and her few years, and her childish aspect.

They were come into the High Street, where the prison stood, when a voice cried, "Little mother, little mother!" Dorrit stopping and looking back, an excited figure of a strange kind bounced against them (still crying "little mother"), fell down, and scattered the contents of a large basket, filled with potatoes, in the mud.

"Oh, Maggy," said Dorrit, "what a clumsy child you are!"

Maggy was not hurt, but picked herself up immediately, and then began to pick up the potatoes, in which both Dorrit and Arthur Clen-

Little mother

nam helped. Maggy picked up very few potatoes, and a great quantity of mud; but they were all recovered, and deposited in the basket. Maggy then smeared her muddy face with her shawl and presenting it to Mr. Clennam as a type of purity, enabled him to see what she was like.

She was about eight-and-twenty, with large bones, large features, large feet and hands, large eyes and no hair. Her large eyes were limpid and almost colourless; they seemed to be very little affected by light, and to stand unnaturally still. There was also that attentive listening expression in her face, which is seen in the faces of the blind; but she was not blind, having one tolerably serviceable eye. Her face was not exceedingly ugly, though it was only redeemed from being so by a smile, a good-humoured smile, and pleasant in itself, but rendered pitiable by being constantly there. A great white cap, with a quantity of opaque frilling that was always flapping about, apologised for Maggy's baldness, and made it so very difficult for her old black bonnet to retain its place upon her head, that it held on round her neck like a gipsy's baby. A commission of haberdashers could alone have reported what the rest of her poor dress was made of; but it had a strong general resemblance to seaweed, with here and there a gigantic tea-leaf. Her shawl looked particularly like a tea-leaf, after long infusion.

Arthur Clennam looked at Dorrit, with the expression of one saying, "May I ask who this is?" Dorrit, whose hand this Maggy, still calling her little mother, had begun to fondle, answered in words (they were under a gateway into which the majority of the potatoes had rolled).

"This is Maggy, sir."

"Maggy, sir," echoed the personage presented. "Little mother!"

"She is the grand-daughter –" said Dorrit.

"Grand-daughter," echoed Maggy.

"Of my old nurse, who has been dead a long time. Maggy, how old are you?"

"Ten, mother," said Maggy.

"You can't think how good she is, sir," said Dorrit, with infinite tenderness.

"Good *she* is," echoed Maggy, transferring the pronoun in a most expressive way from herself to her little mother.

"Oh how clever," said Dorrit. "She goes on errands as well as any one." Maggy laughed. "And is as trustworthy as the Bank of England." Maggy laughed. "She earns her own living entirely. Entirely, sir!" said Dorrit in a lower and triumphant tone. "Really does!"

"What is her history?" asked Clennam.

"Think of that, Maggy?" said Dorrit, taking her two large hands and clapping them together. "A gentleman from thousands of miles away, wanting to know your history!"

"*My* history?" cried Maggy. "Little mother."

"She means me," said Dorrit, rather confused; "she is very much attached to me. Her old grandmother was not so kind to her as she should have been; was she, Maggy?"

Maggy shook her head, made a drinking vessel of her clenched left hand, drank out of it, and said, "Gin." Then beat an imaginary child, and said, "Broom-handles and pokers."

"When Maggy was ten years old," said Dorrit, watching her face while she spoke, "she had a bad fever, sir, and she has never grown any older ever since."

"Ten years old," said Maggy, nodding her head. "But what a nice hospital! So comfortable, wasn't it? Oh so nice it was. Such a Ev'nly place!"

"She had never been at peace before, sir," said Dorrit, turning towards Arthur for an instant and speaking low, "and she always runs off upon that."

"Such beds there is there!" cried Maggy. "Such lemonades! Such oranges! Such d'licious broth and wine! Such Chicking! Oh, AIN'T it a delightful place to go and stop at!"

"So Maggy stopped there as long as she could," said Dorrit, in her former tone of telling a child's story; the tone designed for Maggy's ear, "and at last, when she could stop there no longer, she came out. Then, because she was never to be more than ten years old, however long she lived – "

"However long she lived," echoed Maggy.

"And because she was very weak; indeed was so weak that when she began to laugh she couldn't stop herself – which was a great pity – "

(Maggy mighty grave of a sudden.)

"Her grandmother did not know what to do with her, and for some years was very unkind to her indeed. At length, in course of time, Maggy began to take pains to improve herself, and to be very attentive and very industrious; and by degrees was allowed to come in and out as often as she liked, and got enough to do to support herself, and does support herself. And that," said Little Dorrit, clapping the two great hands together again, "is Maggy's history, as Maggy knows!"

Little Dorrit, *Chapter 9 (Book 1)*

Youth Opportunity

Mr. Gamfield, a chimney sweep, is in search of an apprentice.

"THIS HERE boy, sir, wot the parish wants to 'prentis," said Mr. Gamfield.

"Ay, my man," said the gentleman in the white waistcoat, with a condescending smile. "What of him?"

"If the parish vould like him to learn a right pleasant trade, in a good 'spectable chimbley-sweepin' bisness," said Mr. Gamfield, "I wants a 'prentis, and I am ready to take him."

"Walk in," said the gentleman in the white waistcoat. Mr. Gamfield having lingered behind, to give the donkey another blow on the head, and another wrench of the jaw, as a caution not to run away in his absence, followed the gentleman with the white waistcoat into the room where Oliver had first seen him.

"It's a nasty trade," said Mr. Limbkins, when Gamfield had again stated his wish.

"Young boys have been smothered in chimneys before now," said another gentleman.

"That's acause they damped the straw afore they lit it in the chimbley to make 'em come down agin," said Gamfield; "that's all smoke, and no blaze; vereas smoke ain't o' no use at all in making a boy come down, for it only sinds him to sleep, and that's wot he likes. Boys is wery obstinit, and wery lazy, gen'lmen, and there's nothink like a good hot blaze to make 'em come down vith a run. It's humane too, gen'lmen, acause, even if they've stuck in the chimbley, roasting their feet makes 'em struggle to hextricate theirselves."

Oliver Twist, *Chapter 3*

Cultivating the Young

Doctor Blimber is another of Dickens's damaging schoolmasters. He presides over an Academy where pupils are 'crammed' with knowledge.

WHENEVER a young gentleman was taken in hand by Doctor Blimber, he might consider himself sure of a pretty tight squeeze. The Doctor only undertook the charge of ten young gentlemen, but he had, always ready, a supply of learning for a hundred, on the lowest estimate; and it was at once the business and delight of his life to gorge the unhappy ten with it.

In fact, Doctor Blimber's establishment was a great hothouse, in which there was a forcing apparatus incessantly at work. All the boys blew before their time. Mental green peas were produced at Christmas, and intellectual asparagus all the year round. Mathematical gooseberries (very sour ones too) were common at untimely seasons, and from mere sprouts of bushes, under Doctor Blimber's cultivation. Every description of Greek and Latin vegetable was got off the driest twigs of boys, under the frostiest circumstances. Nature was of no consequence at all. No matter what a young gentleman was intended to bear, Doctor Blimber made him bear to pattern, somehow or other.

Dombey and Son, *Chapter 11*

COMIC AND CURIOUS

An invitation for Mr. Pickwick

The Pickwick Papers is not really a novel but the comic spirit of the book endures, though gradually darkening, throughout Dickens's writing career. The Pickwick Papers comprises a series of adventures that Mr. Pickwick and his friends (the improbably named Nathaniel Winkle, Tracy Tupman and Augustus Snodgrass) have as members of an antiquarian club. Vital to the success of the book was Mr. Pickwick's manservant, Sam Weller, who appears here briefly and makes a more substantial appearance in another passage (see page 66). The Pickwick Papers was serialised in twenty monthly parts, something 'serious' writers did not do until the success of this, and later books by Dickens published in this way, led other novelists to follow suit. Dickens was twenty-four when Pickwick began. A year later he was a celebrity.

MR. PICKWICK's conscience had been somewhat reproaching him for his recent neglect of his friends at the Peacock; and he was just on the point of walking forth in quest of them, on the third morning after the election had terminated, when his faithful valet put into his hand a card, on which was engraved the following inscription:

Mrs. Leo Hunter*,
The Den. Eatanswill.

"Person's a waitin'," said Sam, epigrammatically.

"Does the person want me, Sam?" inquired Mr. Pickwick.

"He wants you particklar; and no one else'll do, as the Devil's private secretary said ven he fetched avay Doctor Faustus," replied Mr. Weller.

"*He*. Is it a gentleman?" said Mr. Pickwick.

"A wery good imitation o' one, if it an't," replied Mr. Weller.

"But this is a lady's card," said Mr. Pickwick.

"Given me by a gen'lm'n hows'ever," replied Sam, "and he's waitin' in the drawing-room – said he'd rather wait all day, than not see you."

Mr. Pickwick, on hearing this determination, descended to the draw-

* Mrs. Leo Hunter: there is a pun in the name. Dickens knew from experience as well as observation what it was to be lionised (fawned on by people because he was well known).

ing-room, where sat a grave man, who started up on his entrance, and said, with an air of profound respect:

"Mr. Pickwick, I presume?"

"The same."

"Allow me, sir, the honour of grasping your hand. Permit me, sir, to shake it," said the grave man.

"Certainly," said Mr. Pickwick.

The stranger shook the extended hand, and then continued.

"We have heard of your fame, sir. The noise of your antiquarian discussion has reached the ears of Mrs. Leo Hunter – my wife, sir; *I* am *Mr.* Leo Hunter" – the stranger paused, as if he expected that Mr. Pickwick would be overcome by the disclosure; but seeing that he remained perfectly calm, proceeded.

"My wife, sir – Mrs. Leo Hunter – is proud to number among her acquaintance all those who have rendered themselves celebrated by their works and talents. Permit me, sir, to place in a conspicuous part of the list the name of Mr. Pickwick, and his brother members of the club that derives its name from him."

"I shall be extremely happy to make the acquaintance of such a lady, sir," replied Mr. Pickwick.

"You *shall* make it, sir," said the grave man. "Tomorrow morning, sir, we give a public breakfast – a *fête champêtre** – to a great number of those who have rendered themselves celebrated by their works and talents. Permit Mrs. Leo Hunter, sir, to have the gratification of seeing you at the Den."

"With great pleasure," replied Mr. Pickwick.

"Mrs. Leo Hunter has many of these breakfasts, sir," resumed the new acquaintance – " 'feasts of reason, sir, and flows of soul,' as somebody who wrote a sonnet to Mrs. Leo Hunter on her breakfasts, feelingly and originally observed."

"Was *he* celebrated for his works and talents?" inquired Mr. Pickwick.

"He was, sir," replied the grave man, "all Mrs. Leo Hunter's acquaintance are; it is her ambition, sir, to have no other acquaintance."

"It is a very noble ambition," said Mr. Pickwick.

"When I inform Mrs. Leo Hunter, that that remark fell from *your* lips, sir, she will indeed be proud," said the grave man. "You have a gentleman in your train, who has produced some beautiful little poems, I think, sir."

"My friend Mr. Snodgrass has a great taste for poetry," replied Mr. Pickwick.

"So has Mrs. Leo Hunter, sir. She dotes on poetry, sir. She adores it; I may say that her whole soul and mind are wound up, and entwined with

* *fête champêtre*: an outdoor festival

Mrs. Leo Hunter's Fancy-Dress Déjeuné

it. She has produced some delightful pieces, herself, sir. You may have met with her 'Ode to an expiring Frog,' sir."

"I don't think I have," said Mr. Pickwick.

"You astonish me, sir," said Mr. Leo Hunter. "It created an immense sensation. It was signed with an 'L' and eight stars, and appeared originally in a Lady's Magazine. It commenced

'Can I view thee panting, lying
On thy stomach, without sighing;
Can I unmoved see thee dying
On a log,
Expiring frog!' "

"Beautiful!" said Mr. Pickwick.

"Fine," said Mr. Leo Hunter, "so simple."

"Very," said Mr. Pickwick.

"The next verse is still more touching. Shall I repeat it?"

"If you please," said Mr. Pickwick.

"It runs thus," said the grave man, still more gravely.

" 'Say, have fiends in shape of boys,
With wild halloo, and brutal noise
Hunted thee from marshy joys,
With a dog,
Expiring frog!' "

"Finely expressed," said Mr. Pickwick.

"All point, sir," said Mr. Leo Hunter, "but you shall hear Mrs. Leo Hunter repeat it. *She* can do justice to it, sir. She will repeat it, in character, sir, tomorrow morning."

"In character!"

"As Minerva.* But I forgot – it's a fancy-dress breakfast."

The Pickwick Papers, *Chapter 15*

* Minerva: the Roman goddess of wisdom

A proposal

Esther Summerson is a young woman abandoned as a love-child and in ignorance of her origins. She has a guardian who is visited one day by Mr. Guppy, a lawyer's clerk on the make who has met Esther before and senses (rightly) that she may be well-connected. On the basis of only a slight acquaintance, the clerk astonishes Esther with a proposal of marriage. In **Bleak House** *there are two narrative voices, Esther's and the author's, sharing the chapters equally between them. On this occasion, Esther tells her own story.*

"I BEG your pardon, miss!" said Mr. Guppy, rising when he saw me rise. "But would you allow me the favour of a minute's private conversation?"

Not knowing what to say, I sat down again.

"What follows is without prejudice,* miss?" said Mr. Guppy, anxiously bringing a chair towards my table.

"I don't understand what you mean," said I, wondering.

"It's one of our law terms, miss. You won't make any use of it to my detriment at Kenge and Carboy's or elsewhere. If our conversation shouldn't lead to anything, I am to be as I was and am not to be prejudiced in my situation or worldly prospects. In short, it's in total confidence."

"I am at a loss, sir," said I, "to imagine what you can have to communicate in total confidence to me, whom you have never seen but once; but I should be very sorry to do you any injury."

"Thank you, miss. I'm sure of it – that's quite sufficient."

All this time Mr. Guppy was either planing his forehead with his handkerchief or tightly rubbing the palm of his left hand with the palm of his right. "If you would excuse my taking another glass of wine, miss, I think it might assist me in getting on without a continual choke that cannot fail to be mutually unpleasant."

He did so, and came back again. I took the opportunity of moving well behind my table.

"You wouldn't allow me to offer you one, would you, miss?" said Mr. Guppy, apparently refreshed.

"Not any," said I.

* without prejudice: a legal phrase that prevents a contract from being binding.

"Not half a glass?" said Mr. Guppy. "Quarter? No! Then, to proceed. My present salary, Miss Summerson, at Kenge and Carboy's, is two pound a week. When I first had the happiness of looking upon you, it was one fifteen,* and had stood at that figure for a lengthened period. A rise of five has since taken place, and a further rise of five* is guaranteed at the expiration of a term not exceeding twelve months from the present date. My mother has a little property, which takes the form of a small life annuity, upon which she lives in an independent though unassuming manner in the Old Street Road. She is eminently calculated for a mother-in-law. She never interferes, is all for peace, and her disposition easy. She has her failings – as who has not? – but I never knew her do it when company was present, at which time you may freely trust her with wines, spirits, or malt liquors. My own abode is lodgings at Penton Place, Pentonville. It is lowly, but airy, open at the back, and considered one of the 'ealthiest outlets. Miss Summerson! In the mildest language, I adore you. Would you be so kind as to allow me (as I may say) to file a declaration – to make an offer!"

Mr. Guppy went down on his knees. I was well behind my table and not much frightened. I said, "Get up from that ridiculous position immediately, sir, or you will oblige me to break my implied promise and ring the bell!"

"Hear me out, miss!" said Mr. Guppy, folding his hands.

"I cannot consent to hear another word, sir," I returned, "unless you get up from the carpet directly and go and sit down at the table as you ought to do if you have any sense at all."

He looked piteously, but slowly rose and did so.

"Yet what a mockery it is, miss," he said with his hand upon his heart and shaking his head at me in a melancholy manner over the tray, "to be stationed behind food at such a moment. The soul recoils from food at such a moment, miss."

"I beg you to conclude," said I; "you have asked me to hear you out, and I beg you to conclude."

"I will, miss," said Mr. Guppy. "As I love and honour, so likewise I will obey. Would that I could make thee the subject of that vow before the shrine!"

"That is quite impossible," said I, "and entirely out of the question."

"I am aware," said Mr. Guppy, leaning forward over the tray and regarding me, as I again strangely felt, though my eyes were not directed to him, with his late intent look, "I am aware that in a worldly point of view, according to all appearances, my offer is a poor one. But, Miss

* one fifteen: one pound, fifteen shillings (£1.75 in decimal currency but worth much more then, of course, in living terms).

* five: five shillings (25 p)

Guppy declares his love

Summerson! Angel! No, don't ring – I have been brought up in a sharp school and am accustomed to a variety of general practice. Though a young man, I have ferreted out evidence, got up cases, and seen lots of life. Blest with your hand, what means might I not find of advancing your interests and pushing your fortunes! What might I not get to know, nearly concerning you? I know nothing now, certainly; but what *might* I not if I had your confidence, and you set me on?''

I told him that he addressed my interest or what he supposed to be my interest quite as unsuccessfully as he addressed my inclination, and he would now understand that I requested him, if he pleased, to go away immediately.

"Cruel miss," said Mr. Guppy, "hear but another word! I think you must have seen that I was struck with those charms on the day when I waited at the Whytorseller*. I think you must have remarked that I could not forbear a tribute to those charms when I put up the steps of the 'ackney-coach. It was a feeble tribute to thee, but it was well meant. Thy image has ever since been fixed in my breast. I have walked up and down of an evening opposite Jellyby's house only to look upon the bricks

* Whytorseller: the White Horse cellar, the scene of Mr. Guppy's only previous meeting with Esther.

that once contained thee. This out of today, quite an unnecessary out so far as the attendance, which was its pretended object, went, was planned by me alone for thee alone. If I speak of interest, it is only to recommend myself and my respectful wretchedness. Love was before it, and is before it."

"I should be pained, Mr. Guppy," said I, rising and putting my hand upon the bell-rope, "to do you or any one who was sincere the injustice of slighting any honest feeling, however disagreeably expressed. If you have really meant to give me a proof of your good opinion, though ill-timed and misplaced, I feel that I ought to thank you. I have very little reason to be proud, and I am not proud. I hope," I think I added, without very well knowing what I said, "that you will now go away as if you had never been so exceedingly foolish and attend to Messrs. Kenge and Carboy's business."

"Half a minute, miss!" cried Mr. Guppy, checking me as I was about to ring. "This has been without prejudice?"

"I will never mention it," said I, "unless you should give me future occasion to do so."

"A quarter of a minute, miss! In case you should think better at any time, however distant – *that's* no consequence, for my feelings can never alter – of anything I have said, particularly what might I not do, Mr. William Guppy, eighty-seven, Penton Place, or if removed, or dead (of blighted hopes or anything of that sort), care of Mrs. Guppy, three hundred and two, Old Street Road, will be sufficient."

I rang the bell, the servant came, and Mr. Guppy, laying his written card upon the table and making a dejected bow, departed.

Bleak House, *Chapter 9*

Mrs. Gamp

Martin Chuzzlewit was written after Dickens visited America in 1842 and his satirical presentation of American life in part of the book caused offence there.

The character of Mrs. Gamp, like many another from Dickens's novels, has entered folklore. The point about her friend Mrs. Harris and the cartoon accompanying the passage (see page 64), is that the friend does not exist except as a perpetual character reference made up by Mrs. Gamp for herself. Mr. Pecksniff is a hypocritical and avaricious architect who is full of virtuous precepts: one of Dickens's many confidence tricksters. He has two daughters, Charity and Mercy, to match.

"WHAT, MR. WHILKS!" cried Mrs. Gamp. "Don't say it's you, Mr. Whilks, and that poor creetur Mrs. Whilks with not even a pin-cushion ready. Don't say it's you, Mr. Whilks!"

"It isn't Mr. Whilks," said Pecksniff. "I don't know the man. Nothing of the kind. A gentleman is dead; and some person being wanted in the house, you have been recommended by Mr. Mould the undertaker."

As she was by this time in a condition to appear, Mrs. Gamp, who had a face for all occasions, looked out of the window with her mourning countenance, and said she would be down directly. But the matrons took it very ill that Mr. Pecksniff's mission was of so unimportant a kind; and the lady with her arms folded rated him in good round terms, signifying that she would be glad to know what he meant by terrifying delicate females "with his corpses": and giving it as her opinion that he was quite ugly enough to know better. The other ladies were not at all behind-hand in expressing similar sentiments; and the children, of whom some scores had now collected, hooted and defied Mr. Pecksniff quite savagely. So when Mrs. Gamp appeared, the unoffending gentleman was glad to hustle her with very little ceremony into the cabriolet, and drive off, overwhelmed with popular execration.

Mrs. Gamp had a large bundle with her, a pair of pattens*, and a species of gig umbrella; the latter article in colour like a faded leaf, except where a circular patch of a lively blue had been dexterously let in at the top. She was much flurried by the haste she had made, and laboured under the most erroneous views of cabriolets, which she

* pattens: wooden overshoes, to raise the wearer above the mud of the streets.

appeared to confound with mail-coaches or stage-waggons, inasmuch as she was constantly endeavouring for the first half mile to force her luggage through the little front window, and clamouring to the driver to "put it in the boot". When she was disabused of this idea, her whole being resolved itself into an absorbing anxiety about her pattens, with which she played innumerable games at quoits on Mr. Pecksniff's legs. It was not until they were close upon the house of mourning that she had enough composure to observe:

"And so the gentleman's dead, sir! Ah! The more's the pity." She didn't even know his name. "But it's what we must all come to. It's as certain as being born, except that we can't make our calculations as exact. Ah! Poor dear!"

Mr. Pecksniff on his mission

She was a fat old woman, this Mrs. Gamp, with a husky voice and a moist eye, which she had a remarkable power of turning up, and only showing the white of it. Having very little neck, it cost her some trouble to look over herself, if one may say so, at those to whom she talked. She wore a very rusty black gown, rather the worse for snuff, and a shawl and bonnet to correspond. In these dilapidated articles of dress she had, on principle, arrayed herself, time out of mind, on such occasions as the present; for this at once expressed a decent amount of veneration for the deceased, and invited the next of kin to present her with a fresher suit of weeds: an appeal so frequently successful, that the very fetch and ghost of Mrs. Gamp, bonnet and all, might be seen hanging up, any hour in the day, in at least a dozen of the second-hand clothes shops about Holborn. The face of Mrs. Gamp – the nose in particular – was

Mrs. Gamp meets Mrs. Harris

somewhat red and swollen, and it was difficult to enjoy her society without becoming conscious of a smell of spirits. Like most persons who have attained to great eminence in their profession, she took to hers very kindly; insomuch that, setting aside her natural predilections as a woman, she went to a lying-in or a laying-out with equal zest and relish.

"Ah!" repeated Mrs. Gamp; for it was always a safe sentiment in cases of mourning. "Ah dear! When Gamp was summoned to his long home, and I see him a-lying in Guy's Hospital with a penny-piece* on each eye, and his wooden leg under his left arm, I thought I should have fainted away. But I bore up."

If certain whispers current in the Kingsgate Street circles had any truth in them, she had indeed borne up surprisingly; and had exerted such uncommon fortitude as to dispose of Mr. Gamp's remains for the benefit of science.* But it should be added, in fairness, that this had happened twenty years before; and that Mr. and Mrs. Gamp had long been separated on the ground of incompatibility of temper in their drink.

"You have become indifferent since then, I suppose?" said Mr. Pecksniff. "Use is second nature, Mrs. Gamp."

"You may well say second natur, sir," returned that lady. "One's first ways is to find sich things a trial to the feelings, and so is one's lasting custom. If it wasn't for the nerve a little sip of liquor gives me (I never was able to do more than taste it), I never could go through with what I sometimes has to do. 'Mrs. Harris,' I says, at the very last case as ever I acted in, which it was but a young person, 'Mrs. Harris,' I says, 'leave the bottle on the chimley-piece, and don't ask me to take none, but let me put my lips to it when I am so dispoged, and then I will do what I'm engaged to do, according to the best of my ability.' 'Mrs. Gamp,' she says, in answer, 'if ever there was a sober creetur to be got at eighteen pence a day for working people, and three and six for gentlefolks – night watching,' " said Mrs. Gamp, with emphasis, " 'being a extra charge – you are that inwallable person.' 'Mrs. Harris,' I says to her, 'don't name the charge, for if I could afford to lay all my feller creeturs out for nothink, I would gladly do it, sich is the love I bears 'em. But what I always says to them as has the management of matters, Mrs. Harris:' " here she kept her eye on Mr. Pecksniff: " 'be they gents or be they ladies, is, don't ask me whether I won't take none, or whether I will, but leave the bottle on the chimley-piece, and let me put my lips to it when I am so dispoged.' "

Martin Chuzzlewit, *Chapter 19*

* penny-piece: used to keep eyelids closed on someone who has recently died.

* benefit of science: for dissection and anatomy lessons at medical schools.

Principle

Mr. Pickwick has been imprisoned because of a refusal to pay damages which he could easily afford, in a breach of promise action brought against him. His innocence has not protected him from the law and some unscrupulous lawyers, so he accepts imprisonment as a matter of principle. His worldly wise manservant, Sam Weller, arranges out of loyalty to be imprisoned too with the connivance of his father. Sam's tale about a principled man passes its own comment on his master's stubbornness.

"COME IN," said Mr. Pickwick.

Sam appeared, pulled off his hat, and smiled.

"Ah, Sam, my good lad!" said Mr. Pickwick, evidently delighted to see his humble friend again; "I had no intention of hurting your feelings yesterday, my faithful fellow, by what I said. Put down your hat, Sam, and let me explain my meaning, a little more at length."

"Won't presently do, sir?" inquired Sam.

"Certainly," said Mr. Pickwick; "but why not now?"

"I'd rayther not now, sir," rejoined Sam.

"Why?" inquired Mr. Pickwick.

"'Cause – " said Sam, hesitating.

"Because of what?" inquired Mr. Pickwick, alarmed at his follower's manner. "Speak out, Sam."

"'Cause," rejoined Sam; "'cause I've got a little bisness as I want to do."

"What business?" inquired Mr. Pickwick, surprised at Sam's confused manner.

"Nothin' partickler, sir," replied Sam.

"Oh if it's nothing particular," said Mr. Pickwick, with a smile, "you can speak with me first."

"I think I'd better see arter it at once," said Sam, still hesitating.

Mr. Pickwick looked amazed, but said nothing.

"The fact is," said Sam, stopping short.

"Well!" said Mr. Pickwick. "Speak out, Sam."

"Why, the fact is," said Sam, with a desperate effort, "P'raps I'd better see arter my bed afore I do anythin' else."

"*Your bed!*" exclaimed Mr. Pickwick, in astonishment.

"Yes, my bed, sir," replied Sam. "I'm a pris'ner. I was arrested, this here wery arternoon, for debt."

"You arrested for debt!" exclaimed Mr. Pickwick, sinking into a chair.

MR. PICKWICK felt a great deal too much touched by the warmth of Sam's attachment, to be able to exhibit any manifestation of anger or displeasure at the precipitate course he had adopted, in voluntarily consigning himself to a debtors' prison, for an indefinite period. The only point on which he persevered in demanding any explanation, was, the name of Sam's detaining creditor; but this Mr. Weller as perseveringly withheld.

"It ain't o' no use, sir," said Sam, again and again. "He's a malicious, bad-disposed, vorldly minded, spiteful, windictive creetur, with a hard heart as there ain't no soft'nin. As the wirtuous clergyman remarked of the old gen'l'm'n with the dropsy, ven he said, that upon the whole he thought he'd rayther leave his property to his vife than build a chapel vith it."

"But consider, Sam," Mr. Pickwick remonstrated, "the sum is so small that it can very easily be paid; and having made up my mind that you shall stop with me, you should recollect how much more useful you would be, if you could go outside the walls."

"Wery much obliged to you, sir," replied Mr. Weller gravely; "but I'd rayther not."

"Rather not do what, Sam?"

"Wy, I'd rayther not let myself down to ask a favour o' this here unremorseful enemy."

"But it is no favour asking him to take his money, Sam," reasoned Mr. Pickwick.

"Beg your pardon, sir," rejoined Sam; "but it 'ud be a wery great favour to pay it, and he don't deserve none; that's where it is, sir."

Here Mr. Pickwick rubbing his nose with an air of some vexation, Mr. Weller thought it prudent to change the theme of the discourse.

"I takes my determination on principle, sir," remarked Sam, "and you takes yours on the same ground; wich puts me in mind o' the man as killed his-self on principle, wich o' course you've heerd on, sir." Mr. Weller paused when he arrived at this point, and cast a comical look at his master out of the corners of his eyes.

"There is no 'of course' in the case, Sam," said Mr. Pickwick, gradually breaking into a smile, in spite of the uneasiness which Sam's obstinacy had given him. "The fame of the gentleman in question, never reached my ears."

"No, sir!" exclaimed Mr. Weller. "You astonish me, sir; he wos a clerk in a gov'ment office, sir."

"Was he?" said Mr. Pickwick.

"Yes, he wos, sir," rejoined Mr. Weller; "and a wery pleasant gen'l'm'n too – one o' the precise and tidy sort, as puts their feet in little India-rubber fire-buckets wen it's wet weather, and never has no other bosom friends but hare-skins; he saved up his money on principle, wore a clean shirt ev'ry day on principle; never spoke to none of his relations on principle, 'fear they shou'd want to borrow money of him; and wos altogether, in fact, an uncommon agreeable character. He had his hair cut on principle vunce a fortnight, and contracted for his clothes on the economic principle – three suits a year, and send back the old uns. Being a wery reg'lar gen'l'm'n, he din'd ev'ry day at the same place, where it wos one and nine to cut off the joint, and a wery good one and nine's worth he used to cut, as the landlord often said, with the tears a tricklin' down his face: let alone the way he used to poke the fire in the vinter time, which wos a dead loss o' four-pence ha'penny a day: to say nothin' at all o' the aggrawation o' seein' him do it. So uncommon grand with it too! 'Post arter the next gen'l'm'n,' he sings out ev'ry day ven he comes in. 'See arter the *Times*, Thomas, let me look at the *Mornin' Herald*, wen it's out o' hand; don't forget to bespeak the *Chronicle*; and just bring the '*Tiser*,* vill you:' and then he'd set vith his eyes fixed on the clock, and rush out, just a quarter of a minit afore the time, to waylay the boy as wos a comin' in with the evenin' paper, wich he'd read with sich intense interest and persewerance as worked the other customers up to the wery confines o' desperation and insanity, 'specially one i-rascible old gen'l'm'n as the vaiter wos always obliged to keep a sharp eye on, at sich times, fear he should be tempted to commit some rash act with the carving knife. Vell, sir, here he'd stop, occupyin' the best place for three hours, and never takin' nothin' arter his dinner, but sleep, and then he'd go away to a coffee house a few streets off, and have a small pot o' coffee and four crumpets, arter wich he'd walk home to Kensington and go to bed. One night he wos took very ill; sends for a doctor; doctor comes in a green fly, with a kind o' Robinson Crusoe set o' steps, as he could let down wen he got out, and pull up arter him wen he got in, to perwent the necessity o' the coachman's gettin' down, and thereby undeceivin' the public by lettin' 'em see that it wos only a livery coat as he'd got on, and not the trousers to match. 'Wot's the matter?' says the doctor. 'Wery ill,' says the patient. 'Wot have you been a eatin' on?' says the doctor. 'Roast weal,' says the patient. 'Wot's the last thing you dewoured?' says the doctor. 'Crumpets,' says the patient. 'That's it!' says the doctor. 'I'll send you a box of pills directly, and don't you never take no more of

* *Times*, etc.: newspapers (one of which, the *Morning Chronicle*, Dickens was a reporter on for two years), except the *Morning Advertiser* (the '*Tiser*) which was a brewers' and publicans' trade journal.

'em,' he says. 'No more o' wot?' says the patient – 'Pills?' 'No; crumpets,' says the doctor. 'Wy?' says the patient, starting up in bed; 'I've eat four crumpets, ev'ry night for fifteen year, on principle.' 'Well, then, you'd better leave 'em off, on principle,' says the doctor. 'Crumpets is wholesome, sir,' says the patient. 'Crumpets is *not* wholesome, sir,' says the doctor, wery fierce. 'But they're so cheap,' says the patient, comin' down a little, 'and so wery fillin' at the price.' 'They'd be dear to you, at any price; dear if you wos paid to eat 'em,' says the doctor. 'Four crumpets a night,' he says, 'vill do your business in six months!' The patient looks him full in the face, and turns it over in his mind for a long time, and at last he says, 'Are you sure o' that 'ere, sir?' 'I'll stake my professional reputation on it,' says the doctor. 'How many crumpets, at a sittin', do you think 'ud kill me off at once?' says the patient. 'I don't know,' says the doctor. 'Do you think half a crown's wurth 'ud do it?' says the patient. 'I think it might,' says the doctor. 'Three shillins' wurth 'ud be sure to do it, I s'pose?' says the patient. 'Certainly,' says the doctor. 'Wery good,' says the patient; 'good night.' Next mornin' he gets up, has a fire lit, orders in three shillins' wurth o' crumpets, toasts 'em all, eats 'em all, and blows his brains out."

"What did he do that for?" inquired Mr. Pickwick abruptly; for he was considerably startled by this tragical termination of the narrative.

"Wot did he do it for, sir?" reiterated Sam. "Wy in support of his great principle that crumpets wos wholesome, and to show that he wouldn't be put out of his way for nobody!"

The Pickwick Papers, *Chapters 43 and 44*

Hamlet

Dickens was a passionate theatre-goer and as a young man was close to taking up acting as a career. He regularly organised and took part in amateur theatricals with his family and friends and there are many testimonies as to how good he was. He probably knew most of the theatres in London from the grand ones, such as the Covent Garden (now the Opera House) and Drury Lane, to the lowest 'penny gaffs' where the entertainment was of the crudest kind.

In this scene from ***Great Expectations****, Pip, the hero of the book and now twenty, goes to a minor theatre in London accompanied by his friend Herbert Pocket to see an acquaintance from Pip's childhood perform in a production of* ***Hamlet****.*

On our arrival in Denmark, we found the king and queen of that country elevated in two armchairs on a kitchen-table, holding a Court. The whole of the Danish nobility were in attendance; consisting of a noble boy in the wash-leather boots of a gigantic ancestor, a venerable Peer with a dirty face who seemed to have risen from the people late in life, and the Danish chivalry with a comb in its hair and a pair of white silk legs, and presenting on the whole a feminine appearance. My gifted townsman stood gloomily apart, with folded arms, and I could have wished that his curls and forehead had been more probable.

Several curious little circumstances transpired as the action proceeded. The late king of the country not only appeared to have been troubled with a cough at the time of his decease, but to have taken it with him to the tomb, and to have brought it back. The royal phantom also carried a ghostly manuscript round its truncheon, to which it had the appearance of occasionally referring, and that, too, with an air of anxiety and a tendency to lose the place of reference which were suggestive of a state of mortality. It was this, I conceive, which led to the Shade's being advised by the gallery to "turn over!" – a recommendation which it took extremely ill. It was likewise to be noted of this majestic spirit that whereas it always appeared with an air of having been out a long time and walked an immense distance, it perceptibly came from a closely contiguous wall. This occasioned its terrors to be received derisively. The Queen of Denmark, a very buxom lady, though no doubt historically brazen, was considered by the public to have too much brass about her; her chin being attached to her diadem by a broad band of that metal (as if she had a gorgeous toothache), her waist being encircled by another, and each of her arms by another, so that she was openly mentioned as "the kettledrum". The noble boy in the ancestral boots, was inconsistent; representing himself, as it were in one breath, as an able seaman, a strolling actor, a grave-digger, a clergyman, and a person of the utmost importance at a Court fencing-match, on the authority of whose practised eye and nice discrimination the finest strokes were judged. This gradually led to a want of toleration for him, and even – on his being detected in holy orders, and declining to perform the funeral service – to the general indignation taking the form of nuts. Lastly, Ophelia was a prey to such slow musical madness, that when, in course of time, she had taken off her white muslin scarf, folded it up, and buried it, a sulky man who had been long cooling his impatient nose against an iron bar in the front row of the gallery, growled, "Now the baby's put to bed let's have supper!" Which, to say the least of it, was out of keeping.

Upon my unfortunate townsman all these incidents accumulated with playful effect. Whenever that undecided Prince had to ask a question or state a doubt, the public helped him out with it. As for example; on the question whether 'twas nobler in the mind to suffer, some roared yes, and some no, and some inclining to both opinions said 'toss up for it'; and quite a Debating Society arose. When he asked what should such fellows as he do crawling between earth and heaven, he was encouraged with loud cries of 'Hear, hear!' When he appeared with his stocking disordered (its disorder expressed, according to usage, by one very neat fold in the top, which I suppose to be always got up with a flat iron), a conversation took place in the gallery respecting the paleness of his leg, and whether it was occasioned by the turn the ghost had given him. On his taking the recorders – very like a little black flute that had just been played in the orchestra and handed out at the door – he was called upon unanimously for Rule Britannia. When he recommended the player not to saw the air thus, the sulky man said, 'And don't *you* do it, neither; you're a deal worse than *him*!' And I grieve to add that peals of laughter greeted Mr. Wopsle on every one of these occasions.

But his greatest trials were in the churchyard: which had the appearance of a primeval forest, with a kind of small ecclesiastical wash-house on one side, and a turnpike gate on the other. Mr. Wopsle in a comprehensive black cloak, being descried entering at the turnpike, the gravedigger was admonished in a friendly way, "Look out! Here's the undertaker a coming, to see how you're a getting on with your work!" I believe it is well known in a constitutional country that Mr. Wopsle could not possibly have returned the skull, after moralising over it, without dusting his fingers on a white napkin taken from his breast; but even that innocent and indispensable action did not pass without the comment 'Wai-ter!' The arrival of the body for interment (in an empty black box with the lid tumbling open), was the signal for a general joy which was much enhanced by the discovery, among the bearers, of an individual obnoxious to identification. The joy attended Mr. Wopsle through his struggle with Laertes on the brink of the orchestra and the grave, and slackened no more until he had tumbled the king off the kitchen-table, and had died by inches from the ankles upward.

We had made some pale efforts in the beginning to applaud Mr. Wopsle; but they were too hopeless to be persisted in. Therefore we had sat, feeling keenly for him, but laughing, nevertheless, from ear to ear. I laughed in spite of myself all the time, the whole thing was so droll; and yet I had a latent impression that there was something decidedly fine in Mr. Wopsle's elocution – not for old associations' sake, I am afraid, but because it was very slow, very dreary, very up-hill and down-hill, and very unlike any way in which any man in any natural circumstances of life or death ever expressed himself about anything. When the tragedy was over, and he had been called for and hooted, I said to Herbert, "Let us go at once, or perhaps we shall meet him."

We made all the haste we could downstairs, but we were not quick enough either. Standing at the door was a Jewish man with an unnatural heavy smear of eyebrow, who caught my eyes as we advanced, and said, when we came up with him:

"Mr. Pip and friend?"

Identity of Mr. Pip and friend confessed.

"Mr. Waldengarver," said the man, "would be glad to have the honour."

"Waldengarver?" I repeated – when Herbert murmured in my ear, "Probably Wopsle."

"Oh!" said I. "Yes. Shall we follow you?"

"A few steps, please." When we were in a side alley, he turned and asked, "How did you think he looked? – *I* dressed him."

I don't know what he had looked like, except a funeral; with the addition of a large Danish sun or star hanging round his neck by a blue ribbon, that had given him the appearance of being insured in some extraordinary Fire Office.* But I said he had looked very nice.

"When he came to the grave," said our conductor, "he showed his cloak beautiful. But, judging from the wing, it looked to me that when he see the ghost in the queen's apartment, he might have made more of his stockings."

* Fire Office: Fire Insurance. Dickens insured property with the Sun Fire Office, the emblem of which he refers to here.

I modestly assented, and we all fell through a little dirty swing door, into a sort of hot packing-case immediately behind it. Here Mr. Wopsle was divesting himself of his Danish garments, and here there was just room for us to look at him over one another's shoulders, by keeping the packing-case door, or lid, wide open.

"Gentlemen," said Mr. Wopsle, "I am proud to see you. I hope, Mr. Pip, you will excuse my sending round. I had the happiness to know you in former times, and the Drama has ever had a claim which has ever been acknowledged, on the noble and the affluent."

Meanwhile, Mr. Waldengarver, in a frightful perspiration, was trying to get himself out of his princely sables.

"Skin the stockings off, Mr. Waldengarver," said the owner of that property, "or you'll bust 'em. Bust 'em, and you'll bust five-and-thirty shillings. Shakespeare never was complimented with a finer pair. Keep quiet in your chair now, and leave 'em to me."

With that, he went upon his knees, and began to flay his victim; who, on the first stocking coming off, would certainly have fallen over backward with his chair, but for there being no room to fall anyhow.

I had been afraid until then to say a word about the play. But then, Mr. Waldengarver looked up at us complacently, and said:

"Gentlemen, how did it seem to you, to go, in front?"

Herbert said from behind (at the same time poking me), "capitally". So I said "capitally".

"How did you like my reading of the character, gentlemen?" said Mr. Waldengarver, almost, if not quite, with patronage.

Herbert said from behind (again poking me), "massive and concrete". So I said boldly, as if I had originated it, and must beg to insist upon it, "massive and concrete".

"I am glad to have your approbation, gentlemen," said Mr. Waldengarver, with an air of dignity, in spite of his being ground against the wall at the time, and holding on by the seat of the chair.

"But I'll tell you one thing, Mr. Waldengarver," said the man who was on his knees, "in which you're out in your reading. Now mind! I don't care who says contrairy; I tell you so. You're out in your reading of Hamlet when you get your legs in profile."

Great Expectations, *Chapter 31*

Mr. F's Aunt

*Mr. F's Aunt has no part to play in the plot of **Little Dorrit** but is a brilliant fictional example of senile dementia and contributes to the alienation Arthur Clennam feels in his own country after twenty years abroad.*

Arthur has been invited to dinner by Flora Finching, the widowed daughter of Mr. Casby and the sweetheart of Arthur many years earlier. Arthur's embarrassment at this renewal of contact echoes Dickens's own when meeting in middle-age one of his former loves. The aunt in question has been left to Flora, like a bequest, by Mr. Finching (Mr. F).

THERE WAS a fourth and most original figure in the Patriarchal* tent, who also appeared before dinner. This was an amazing little old woman, with a face like a staring wooden doll too cheap for expression, and a stiff yellow wig perched unevenly on the top of her head, as if the child who owned the doll had driven a tack through it anywhere, so that it only got fastened on. Another remarkable thing in this little old woman was, that the same child seemed to have damaged her face in two or three places with some blunt instrument in the nature of a spoon; her countenance, and particularly the tip of her nose, presenting the phenomena of several dints, generally answering to the bowl of that article. A further remarkable thing in this little old woman was, that she had no name but Mr. F's Aunt.

She broke upon the visitor's view under the following circumstances: Flora said when the first dish was being put on the table, perhaps Mr. Clennam might not have heard that Mr. F had left her a legacy? Clennam in return implied his hope that Mr. F had endowed the wife whom he adored, with the greater part of his worldly substance, if not with all. Flora said, oh yes, she didn't mean that, Mr. F had made a beautiful will, but he had left her as a separate legacy, his Aunt. She then went out of the room to fetch the legacy, and, on her return, rather triumphantly presented "Mr. F's Aunt".

The major characteristics discoverable by the stranger in Mr. F's Aunt, were extreme severity and grim taciturnity; sometimes interrup-

* Patriarchal: Arthur Clennam is in the house of a saintly looking but grasping landlord, Mr. Casby, known as the "Patriarch".

ted by a propensity to offer remarks in a deep warning voice, which, being totally uncalled for by anything said by anybody, and traceable to no association of ideas, confounded and terrified the mind. Mr. F's Aunt may have thrown in these observations on some system of her own, and it may have been ingenious, or even subtle: but the key to it was wanted.

The neatly-served and well-cooked dinner (for everything about the Patriarchal household promoted quiet digestion) began with some soup, some fried soles, a butter-boat of shrimp sauce, and a dish of potatoes. The conversation still turned on the receipt of rents. Mr. F's Aunt, after regarding the company for ten minutes with a malevolent gaze, delivered the following fearful remark:

"When we lived at Henley, Barnes's gander was stole by tinkers."

Mr. Pancks* courageously nodded his head and said, "All right, ma'am." But the effect of this mysterious communication upon Clennam was absolutely to frighten him. And another circumstance invested this old lady with peculiar terrors. Though she was always staring, she never acknowledged that she saw any individual. The polite and attentive stranger would desire, say, to consult her inclinations on the subject of potatoes. His expressive action would be hopelessly lost upon her, and what could he do? No man could say, "Mr. F's Aunt, will you permit me?" Every man retired from the spoon, as Clennam did, cowed and baffled.

There was mutton, a steak, and an apple-pie – nothing in the remotest way connected with ganders – and the dinner went on like a disenchanted feast, as it truly was. Once upon a time Clennam had sat at that table taking no heed of anything but Flora; now the principal heed he took of Flora was to observe, against his will, that she was very fond of porter, that she combined a great deal of sherry with sentiment, and that if she were a little overgrown, it was upon substantial grounds. The last of the Patriarchs had always been a mighty eater, and he disposed of an immense quantity of solid food with the benignity of a good soul who was feeding some one else. Mr. Pancks, who was always in a hurry, and who referred at intervals to a little dirty notebook which he kept beside him (perhaps containing the names of the defaulters he meant to look up by way of dessert), took in his victuals much as if he were coaling; with a good deal of noise, a good deal of dropping about, and a puff and a snort occasionally, as if he were nearly ready to steam away.

All through dinner, Flora combined her present appetite for eating and drinking with her past appetite for romantic love, in a way that made Clennam afraid to lift his eyes from his plate; since he could not look towards her without receiving some glance of mysterious meaning or warning, as if they were engaged in a plot. Mr. F's Aunt sat silently

* Mr. Pancks: Mr. Casby's rent-collector, frequently presented by Dickens as if he were a tug-boat.

defying him with an aspect of the greatest bitterness, until the removal of the cloth and the appearance of the decanters, when she originated another observation – struck into the conversation like a clock, without consulting anybody.

Flora had just said, "Mr. Clennam, will you give me a glass of port for Mr. F's Aunt."

"The Monument near London Bridge," that lady instantly proclaimed, "was put up arter the Great Fire of London; and the Great Fire of London was not the fire in which your uncle George's workshops was burned down."

Mr. Pancks, with his former courage, said, "Indeed, ma'am? All right!" But appearing to be incensed by imaginary contradiction, or other ill-usage, Mr. F's Aunt, instead of relapsing into silence, made the following additional proclamation:

"I hate a fool!"

She imparted to this sentiment, in itself almost Solomonic, so extremely injurious and personal a character by levelling it straight at the visitor's head, that it became necessary to lead Mr. F's Aunt from the room. This was quietly done by Flora; Mr. F's Aunt offering no resistance, but inquiring on her way out, "What he come there for, then?" with implacable animosity.

Little Dorrit, *Chapter 13 (Book 1)*

A shooting party

One of Mr. Pickwick's companions, Mr. Winkle, has a reputation as a sportsman. At Manor Farm, Dingley Dell, where the party is staying, this reputation is put to the test. Mr. Pickwick is talking to his host, Mr. Wardle.

"HALLO!" said Mr. Pickwick in his turn: seeing that his companion was armed with a gun, and that another lay ready on the grass. "What's going forward?"

"Why, your friend and I," replied the host, "are going out rook-shooting before breakfast. He's a very good shot, an't he?"

"I've heard him say he's a capital one," replied Mr. Pickwick; "but I never saw him aim at anything."

"Well," said the host, "I wish he'd come. Joe – Joe!"

The fat boy, who under the exciting influence of the morning did not appear to be more than three parts and a fraction asleep, emerged from the house.

"Go up, and call the gentleman, and tell him he'll find me and Mr. Pickwick in the rookery. Show the gentleman the way there; d'ye hear?"

The boy departed to execute his commission; and the host, carrying both guns like a second Robinson Crusoe, led the way from the garden.

"This is the place," said the old gentleman, pausing after a few minutes' walking in an avenue of trees. The information was unnecessary; for the incessant cawing of the unconscious rooks sufficiently indicated their whereabout.

The old gentleman laid one gun on the ground, and loaded the other.

"Here they are," said Mr. Pickwick; and as he spoke, the forms of Mr. Tupman, Mr. Snodgrass, and Mr. Winkle appeared in the distance. The fat boy, not being quite certain which gentleman he was directed to call, had with peculiar sagacity, and to prevent the possibility of any mistake, called them all.

"Come along," shouted the old gentleman, addressing Mr. Winkle; "a keen hand like you ought to have been up long ago, even to such poor work as this."

Mr. Winkle responded with a forced smile, and took up the spare gun with an expression of countenance which a metaphysical rook, impressed with a foreboding of his approaching death by violence, may be supposed to assume. It might have been keenness, but it looked remarkably like misery.

The old gentleman nodded; and two ragged boys who had been marshalled to the spot under the direction of the infant Lambert,* forthwith commenced climbing up two of the trees.

"What are those lads for?" inquired Mr. Pickwick abruptly. He was rather alarmed; for he was not quite certain but that the distress of the agricultural interest, about which he had often heard a great deal, might have compelled the small boys attached to the soil to earn a precarious and hazardous subsistence by making marks of themselves for inexperienced sportsmen.

"Only to start the game," replied Mr. Wardle, laughing.

"To what?" inquired Mr. Pickwick.

"Why, in plain English to frighten the rooks."

"Oh! is that all?"

"You are satisfied?"

"Quite."

"Very well. Shall I begin?"

"If you please," said Mr. Winkle, glad of any respite.

"Stand aside, then. Now for it."

The boy shouted, and shook a branch with a nest on it.

Half-a-dozen young rooks in violent conversation flew out to ask what the matter was. The old gentleman fired by way of reply. Down fell one bird, and off flew the others.

"Take him up, Joe," said the old gentleman.

There was a smile upon the youth's face as he advanced.

Indistinct visions of rook-pie floated through his imagination. He laughed as he retired with the bird – it was a plump one.

"Now, Mr. Winkle," said the host, reloading his own gun. "Fire away."

Mr. Winkle advanced and levelled his gun. Mr. Pickwick and his friends cowered involuntarily to escape damage from the heavy fall of rooks, which they felt quite certain would be occasioned by the devastating barrel of their friend. There was a solemn pause – a shout – a flapping of wings – a faint click.

"Hallo!" said the old gentleman.

"Won't it go?" inquired Mr. Pickwick.

"Missed fire," said Mr. Winkle, who was very pale: probably from disappointment.

"Odd," said the old gentleman, taking the gun. "Never knew one of them miss fire before. Why, I don't see anything of the cap."*

* infant Lambert: a reference to the fat boy that stemmed from Sam Weller. Lambert was a gaoler who became famous just because he was so fat. At his death he weighed nearly 53 stone (336 kg).

* cap: percussion cap used to explode gunpowder which in turn fired the shot in the days before cartridges were invented.

"Bless my soul," said Mr. Winkle. "I declare I forgot the cap!"

The slight omission was rectified. Mr. Pickwick crouched again. Mr. Winkle stepped forward with an air of determination and resolution; and Mr. Tupman looked out from behind a tree. The boy shouted; four birds flew out. Mr. Winkle fired. There was a scream as of an individual – not a rook – in corporeal anguish. Mr. Tupman had saved the lives of innumerable unoffending birds by receiving a portion of the charge in his left arm.

The Pickwick Papers, *Chapter 7*

Ebenezer Scrooge

A Christmas Carol was the first of Dickens's Christmas Books and was published in 1843. The story of the grasping, miserly Ebenezer Scrooge whose character is transformed by a series of ghostly visitations, is one of the most popular that Dickens ever wrote and he used it often in his famous public readings.

It is Christmas Eve and Scrooge's former business partner, Jacob Marley, is about to come back from the dead after seven years with a warning.

YOU'LL WANT all day tomorrow, I suppose?" said Scrooge.

"If quite convenient, sir."

"It's not convenient," said Scrooge, "and it's not fair. If I was to stop half-a-crown for it, you'd think yourself ill-used, I'll be bound?"

The clerk smiled faintly.

"And yet," said Scrooge, "you don't think *me* ill-used, when I pay a day's wages for no work."

The clerk observed that it was only once a year.

"A poor excuse for picking a man's pocket every twenty-fifth of December!" said Scrooge, buttoning his great-coat to the chin. "But I suppose you must have the whole day. Be here all the earlier next morning."

The clerk promised that he would; and Scrooge walked out with a growl. The office was closed in a twinkling, and the clerk, with the long ends of his white comforter dangling below his waist (for he boasted no great-coat), went down a slide on Cornhill, at the end of a lane of boys, twenty times, in honour of its being Christmas Eve, and then ran home to Camden Town as hard as he could pelt, to play at blindman's-buff.

Scrooge took his melancholy dinner in his usual melancholy tavern; and having read all the newspapers, and beguiled the rest of the evening with his banker's-book, went home to bed. He lived in chambers which had once belonged to his deceased partner. They were a gloomy suite of rooms, in a lowering pile of building up a yard, where it had so little business to be, that one could scarcely help fancying it must have run there when it was a young house, playing at hide-and-seek with other houses, and forgotten the way out again. It was old enough now, and dreary enough, for nobody lived in it but Scrooge, the other rooms being all let out as offices. The yard was so dark that even Scrooge, who knew its every stone, was fain to grope with his hands. The fog and frost so hung about the black gateway of the house, that it seemed as if the Genius of the Weather sat in mournful meditation on the threshold.

Now, it is a fact, that there was nothing at all particular about the knocker on the door, except that it was very large. It is also a fact, that Scrooge had seen it, night and morning, during his whole residence in that place; also that Scrooge had as little of what is called fancy about him as any man in the city of London, even including – which is a bold word – the corporation, aldermen, and livery.* Let it also be borne in mind that Scrooge had not bestowed one thought on Marley, since his last mention of his seven-years' dead partner that afternoon. And then let any man explain to me, if he can, how it happened that Scrooge, having his key in the lock of the door, saw in the knocker, without its undergoing any intermediate process of change – not a knocker, but Marley's face.

Marley's face. It was not in impenetrable shadow as the other objects in the yard were, but had a dismal light about it, like a bad lobster in a dark cellar. It was not angry or ferocious, but looked at Scrooge as Marley used to look: with ghostly spectacles turned up on its ghostly forehead. The hair was curiously stirred, as if by breath or hot air; and, though the eyes were wide open, they were perfectly motionless. That, and its livid colour, made it horrible; but its horror seemed to be in spite of the face and beyond its control, rather than a part of its own expression.

As Scrooge looked fixedly at this phenomenon, it was a knocker again.

To say that he was not startled, or that his blood was not conscious of a terrible sensation to which it had been a stranger from infancy, would be untrue. But he put his hand upon the key he had relinquished, turned it sturdily, walked in, and lighted his candle.

He *did* pause, with a moment's irresolution, before he shut the door; and he *did* look cautiously behind it first, as if he half expected to be terrified with the sight of Marley's pigtail sticking out into the hall. But there was nothing on the back of the door, except the screws and nuts that held the knocker on, so he said "Pooh, pooh!" and closed it with a bang.

The sound resounded through the house like thunder. Every room above, and every cask in the wine-merchant's cellars below, appeared to have a separate peal of echoes of its own. Scrooge was not a man to be frightened by echoes. He fastened the door, and walked across the hall, and up the stairs; slowly too: trimming his candle as he went.

You may talk vaguely about driving a coach-and-six up a good old

* livery: i.e. the city guilds

flight of stairs, or through a bad young Act of Parliament; but I mean to say you might have got a hearse up that staircase, and taken it broadwise, with the splinter bar towards the wall and the door towards the balustrades: and done it easy. There was plenty of width for that, and room to spare; which is perhaps the reason why Scrooge thought he saw a locomotive hearse going on before him in the gloom. Half-a-dozen gas-lamps out of the street wouldn't have lighted the entry too well, so you may suppose that it was pretty dark with Scrooge's dip.*

Up Scrooge went, not caring a button for that. Darkness is cheap, and Scrooge liked it. But before he shut his heavy door, he walked through his rooms to see that all was right. He had just enough recollection of the face to desire to do that.

Sitting-room, bedroom, lumber-room. All as they should be. Nobody under the table, nobody under the sofa; a small fire in the grate; spoon and basin ready; and the little saucepan of gruel (Scrooge had a cold in his head) upon the hob. Nobody under the bed; nobody in the closet; nobody in his dressing-gown, which was hanging up in a suspicious attitude against the wall. Lumber-room as usual. Old fire-guard, old shoes, two fish-baskets, washing-stand on three legs, and a poker.

Quite satisfied, he closed his door, and locked himself in; double-locked himself in, which was not his custom. Thus secured against surprise, he took off his cravat; put on his dressing-gown and slippers, and his nightcap; and sat down before the fire to take his gruel.

It was a very low fire indeed; nothing on such a bitter night. He was obliged to sit close to it, and brood over it, before he could extract the least sensation of warmth from such a handful of fuel. The fireplace was an old one, built by some Dutch merchant long ago, and paved all round with quaint Dutch tiles, designed to illustrate the Scriptures. There were Cains and Abels, Pharaoh's daughters, Queens of Sheba, Angelic messengers descending through the air on clouds like feather-beds, Abrahams, Belshazzars, Apostles putting off to sea in butter-boats, hundreds of figures to attract his thoughts; and yet that face of Marley, seven years dead, came like the ancient Prophet's rod*, and swallowed up the whole. If each smooth tile had been a blank at first, with power to shape some picture on its surface from the disjointed fragments of his thoughts, there would have been a copy of old Marley's head on every one.

"Humbug!" said Scrooge; and walked across the room.

After several turns, he sat down again. As he threw his head back in the chair, his glance happened to rest upon a bell, a disused bell, that hung in the room, and communicated for some purpose now forgotten with a chamber in the highest storey of the building. It was with great

* dip: a cheap candle

* Prophet's rod: Aaron's rod in the Old Testament that turned into a serpent.

astonishment, and with a strange, inexplicable dread, that as he looked, he saw this bell begin to swing. It swung so softly in the outset, that it scarcely made a sound; but soon it rang out loudly, and so did every bell in the house.

This might have lasted half a minute, or a minute, but it seemed an hour. The bells ceased as they had begun, together. They were succeeded by a clanking noise, deep down below; as if some person were dragging a heavy chain over the casks in the wine-merchant's cellar. Scrooge then remembered to have heard that ghosts in haunted houses were described as dragging chains.

The cellar-door flew open with a booming sound, and then he heard the noise much louder, on the floors below, then coming up the stairs; then coming straight towards his door.

"It's humbug still!" said Scrooge. "I won't believe it."

His colour changed though, when, without a pause, it came on through the heavy door, and passed into the room before his eyes. Upon its coming in, the dying flame leaped up, as though it cried, "I know him; Marley's Ghost!" and fell again.

The same face: the very same. Marley in his pigtail, usual waistcoat, tights and boots; the tassels on the latter bristling, like his pigtail, and his coat-shirts, and the hair upon his head. The chain he drew was clasped about his middle. It was long, and wound about him like a tail; and it was made (for Scrooge observed it closely) of cash-boxes, keys, padlocks, ledgers, deeds, and heavy purses wrought in steel. His body was transparent; so that Scrooge, observing him, and looking through his waistcoat, could see the two buttons on his coat behind.

Scrooge had often heard it said that Marley had no bowels,* but he had never believed it until now.

No, nor did he believe it even now. Though he looked the phantom through and through, and saw it standing before him; though he felt the chilling influence of its death-cold eyes; and marked the very texture of the folded kerchief bound about its head and chin, which wrapper he had not observed before; he was still incredulous, and fought against his senses.

"How now!" said Scrooge, caustic and cold as ever. "What do you want with me?"

"Much!" – Marley's voice, no doubt about it.

"Who are you?"

"Ask me who I *was*."

"Who *were* you then?" said Scrooge, raising his voice. "You're particular, for a shade." He was going to say "*to* a shade," but substituted this, as more appropriate.

* no bowels: lacking courage (when he was alive)

Marley's ghost

"In life I was your partner, Jacob Marley."

"Can you – can you sit down?" asked Scrooge, looking doubtfully at him.

"I can."

"Do it, then."

Scrooge asked the question, because he didn't know whether a ghost so transparent might find himself in a condition to take a chair; and felt that in the event of its being impossible, it might involve the necessity of an embarrassing explanation. But the ghost sat down on the opposite side of the fireplace, as if he were quite used to it.

"You don't believe in me," observed the Ghost.

"I don't," said Scrooge.

"What evidence would you have of my reality beyond that of your senses?"

"I don't know," said Scrooge.

"Why do you doubt your senses?"

"Because," said Scrooge, "a little thing affects them. A slight disorder of the stomach makes them cheats. You may be an undigested bit of beef, a blot of mustard, a crumb of cheese, a fragment of an underdone potato. There's more of gravy than of grave about you, whatever you are!"

Scrooge was not much in the habit of cracking jokes, nor did he feel, in his heart, by any means waggish then. The truth is, that he tried to be smart, as a means of distracting his own attention, and keeping down his terror; for the spectre's voice disturbed the very marrow in his bones.

To sit, staring at those fixed glazed eyes, in silence for a moment, would play, Scrooge felt, the very deuce with him. There was something very awful, too, in the spectre's being provided with an infernal atmosphere of its own. Scrooge could not feel it himself, but this was clearly the case; for though the Ghost sat perfectly motionless, its hair, and skirts, and tassels, were still agitated as by the hot vapour from an oven.

"You see this toothpick?" said Scrooge, returning quickly to the charge, for the reason just assigned; and wishing, though it were only for a second, to divert the vision's stony gaze from himself.

"I do," replied the Ghost.

"You are not looking at it," said Scrooge.

"But I see it," said the Ghost, "notwithstanding."

"Well!" returned Scrooge, "I have but to swallow this, and be for the rest of my days persecuted by a legion of goblins, all of my own creation. Humbug, I tell you! humbug!"

At this the spirit raised a frightful cry, and shook its chain with such a dismal and appalling noise, that Scrooge held on tight to his chair, to save himself from falling in a swoon. But how much greater was his horror, when the phantom taking off the bandage round its head, as if it were too warm to wear in-doors, its lower jaw dropped down upon its breast.

Scrooge fell upon his knees, and clasped his hands before his face.

"Mercy!" he said. "Dreadful apparition, why do you trouble me?"

"Man of the worldly mind!" replied the Ghost, "do you believe in me or not?"

"I do," said Scrooge. "I must. But why do spirits walk the earth, and why do they come to me?"

"It is required of every man," the Ghost returned, "that the spirit within him should walk abroad among his fellow-men, and travel far and wide; and if that spirit goes not forth in life, it is condemned to do so after death. It is doomed to wander through the world – oh, woe is me! – and witness what it cannot share, but might have shared on earth, and turned to happiness!"

Again the spectre raised a cry, and shook its chain and wrung its shadowy hands.

"You are fettered," said Scrooge, trembling. "Tell me why?"

"I wear the chain I forged in life," replied the Ghost. "I made it link by link, and yard by yard; I girded it on of my own free will, and of my own free will I wore it. Is its pattern strange to *you*?"

Scrooge trembled more and more.

"Or would you know," pursued the Ghost, "the weight and length of the strong coil you bear yourself? It was full as heavy and as long as this, seven Christmas Eves ago. You have laboured on it since. It is a ponderous chain!"

Scrooge glanced about him on the floor, in the expectation of finding himself surrounded by some fifty or sixty fathoms of iron cable: but he could see nothing.

"Jacob," he said, imploringly. "Old Jacob Marley, tell me more. Speak comfort to me, Jacob!"

"I have none to give," the Ghost replied. "It comes from other regions, Ebenezer Scrooge, and is conveyed by other ministers, to other kinds of men. Nor can I tell you what I would. A very little more is all permitted to me. I cannot rest, I cannot stay, I cannot linger anywhere. My spirit never walked beyond our counting-house – mark me! – in life my spirit never roved beyond the narrow limits of our money-changing hole; and weary journeys lie before me!"

It was a habit with Scrooge, whenever he became thoughtful, to put his hands in his breeches pockets. Pondering on what the Ghost had said, he did so now, but without lifting up his eyes, or getting off his knees.

"You must have been very slow about it, Jacob," Scrooge observed, in a business-like manner, though with humility and deference.

"Slow!" the Ghost repeated.

"Seven years dead," mused Scrooge. "And travelling all the time!"

"The whole time," said the Ghost. "No rest, no peace. Incessant torture of remorse."

"You travel fast?" said Scrooge.

"On the wings of the wind," replied the Ghost.

"You might have got over a great quantity of ground in seven years," said Scrooge.

The Ghost, on hearing this, set up another cry, and clanked its chain so hideously in the dead silence of the night, that the Ward would have been justified in indicting it for a nuisance.

"Oh! captive bound, and double-ironed," cried the phantom, "not to know that ages of incessant labour by immortal creatures for this earth must pass into eternity before the good of which it is susceptible is all developed. Not to know that any Christian spirit working kindly in its little sphere, whatever it may be, will find its mortal life too short for its vast means of usefulness. Not to know that no space of regret can make amends for one life's opportunity misused! Yet such was I! Oh such was I!"

"But you were always a good man of business, Jacob," faltered Scrooge, who now began to apply this to himself.

"Business!" cried the Ghost, wringing its hands again. "Mankind was my business. The common welfare was my business; charity, mercy, forbearance, and benevolence, were all my business. The dealings of my trade were but a drop of water in the comprehensive ocean of my business!"

It held up its chain at arm's length, as if that were the cause of all its unavailing grief, and flung it heavily upon the ground again.

"At this time of the rolling year," the spectre said, "I suffer most. Why did I walk through crowds of fellow-beings with my eyes turned down, and never raise them to that blessed Star which led the Wise Men to a poor abode! Were there no poor homes to which its light would have conducted *me*!"

Scrooge was very much dismayed to hear the spectre going on at this rate, and began to quake exceedingly.

"Hear me!" cried the Ghost. "My time is nearly gone."

"I will," said Scrooge. "But don't be hard upon me! Don't be flowery, Jacob! Pray!"

A Christmas Carol, *Stave 1*

Humble and obedient servants

*Dickens's later novels show the author's increasing anger over the incompetence of important public institutions such as the law, parliament and the civil service. The latter was shown to be hopelessly bungling during the Crimean War in the mid-1850s when **Little Dorrit** was written. Dickens refers to the civil service as the Circumlocution Office and Arthur Clennam in his attempts to sort out the affairs of the imprisoned debtor, Mr. Dorrit, meets with bureaucratic obstruction and indifference as he is passed from one department to another.*

"Be so good as to give that card to Mr. Tite Barnacle, and to say that I have just now seen the younger Mr. Barnacle who recommended me to call here."

The footman (who had as many large buttons with the Barnacle crest upon them, on the flaps of his pockets, as if he were the family strong box, and carried the plate and jewels about with him buttoned up) pondered over the card a little; then said, "Walk in." It required some judgment to do it without butting the inner hall-door open, and in the consequent mental confusion and physical darkness slipping down the kitchen stairs. The visitor, however, brought himself up safely on the door-mat.

Still the footman said "Walk in," so the visitor followed him. At the inner hall-door, another bottle seemed to be presented and another stopper taken out. This second vial appeared to be filled with concentrated provisions and extract of Sink from the pantry. After a skirmish in the narrow passage, occasioned by the footman's opening the door of the dismal dining-room with confidence, finding some one there with consternation, and backing on the visitor with disorder, the visitor was shut up, pending his announcement, in a close back parlour. There he had an opportunity of refreshing himself with both the bottles at once, looking out at a low blinding wall three feet off, and speculating on the number of Barnacle families within the bills of mortality* who lived in such hutches of their own free flunkey choice.

Mr. Barnacle would see him. Would he walk up-stairs? He would, and he did; and in the drawing-room, with his leg on a rest, he found Mr.

* bills of mortality: published figures for deaths occurring in the hundred-odd London parishes which made up the area "within the bills of mortality". It is an ironic way of referring to London and its outskirts.

Barnacle himself, the express image and presentment of How not to do it.

Mr. Barnacle dated from a better time, when the country was not so parsimonious and the Circumlocution* Office was not so badgered. He wound and wound folds of white cravat round his neck, as he wound and wound folds of tape and paper round the neck of the country. His wristbands and collar were oppressive; his voice and manner were oppressive. He had a large watch-chain and bunch of seals, a coat buttoned up to inconvenience, a waistcoat buttoned up to inconvenience, an unwrinkled pair of trousers, a stiff pair of boots. He was altogether splendid, massive, over-powering, and impracticable. He seemed to have been sitting for his portrait to Sir Thomas Lawrence* all the days of his life.

"Mr. Clennam?" said Mr. Barnacle. "Be seated."

Mr. Clennam became seated.

"You have called on me, I believe," said Mr. Barnacle, "at the Circumlocution – " giving it the air of a word of about five-and-twenty syllables – "Office."

"I have taken that liberty."

Mr. Barnacle solemnly bent his head as who should say, "I do not deny that it is a liberty; proceed to take another liberty, and let me know your business."

"Allow me to observe that I have been for some years in China, am quite a stranger at home, and have no personal motive or interest in the inquiry I am about to make."

Mr. Barnacle tapped his fingers on the table, and, as if he were now sitting for his portrait to a new and strange artist, appeared to say to his visitor, "If you will be good enough to take me with my present lofty expression, I shall feel obliged."

"I have found a debtor in the Marshalsea Prison of the name of Dorrit, who has been there many years. I wish to investigate his confused affairs so far as to ascertain whether it may not be possible, after this lapse of time, to ameliorate his unhappy condition. The name of Mr. Tite Barnacle has been mentioned to me as representing some highly influential interest among his creditors. Am I correctly informed?"

It being one of the principles of the Circumlocution Office never, on any account whatever, to give a straightforward answer, Mr. Barnacle said, "Possibly."

"On behalf of the Crown, may I ask, or as private individual?"

"The Circumlocution Department, sir," Mr. Barnacle replied, "may have possibly recommended – possibly – I cannot say – that some public

* circumlocution: a roundabout and long-winded way of saying something.

* Sir Thomas Lawrence: a fashionable portrait painter.

claim against the insolvent estate of a firm or co-partnership to which this person may have belonged, should be enforced. The question may have been, in the course of official business, referred to the Circumlocution Department for its consideration. The Department may have either originated, or confirmed, a Minute making that recommendation."

"I assume this to be the case, then."

"The Circumlocution Department," said Mr. Barnacle, "is not responsible for any gentleman's assumptions."

"May I inquire how I can obtain official information as to the real state of the case?"

"It is competent," said Mr. Barnacle, "to any member of the – Public," mentioning that obscure body with reluctance, as his natural enemy, "to memorialise the Circumlocution Department. Such formalities as are required to be observed in so doing, may be known on application to the proper branch of that Department."

"Which is the proper branch?"

"I must refer you," returned Mr. Barnacle, ringing the bell, "to the Department itself for a formal answer to that inquiry."

"Excuse my mentioning – "

"The Department is accessible to the – Public," Mr. Barnacle was always checked a little by that word of impertinent signification, "if the – Public approaches it according to the official forms; if the – Public does not approach it according to the official forms, the – Public has itself to blame."

Mr. Barnacle made him a severe bow, as a wounded man of family, a wounded man of place, and a wounded man of a gentlemanly residence, all rolled into one; and he made Mr. Barnacle a bow, and was shut out into Mews Street by the flabby footman.

Having got to this pass, he resolved as an exercise in perseverance, to betake himself again to the Circumlocution Office, and try what satisfaction he could get there. So he went back to the Circumlocution Office, and once more sent up his card to Barnacle Junior by a messenger who took it very ill indeed that he should come back again, and who was eating mashed potatoes and gravy behind a partition by the hall fire.

He was readmitted to the presence of Barnacle Junior, and found that young gentleman singeing his knees now, and gaping his weary way on to four o'clock.

"I say. Look here. You stick to us in a devil of a manner," said Barnacle Junior, looking over his shoulder.

"I want to know – "

"Look here. Upon my soul you mustn't come into the place saying you want to know, you know," remonstrated Barnacle Junior, turning about and putting up the eye-glass.

"I want to know," said Arthur Clennam, who had made up his mind to persistence in one short form of words, "the precise nature of the claim of the Crown against a prisoner for debt, named Dorrit."

"I say. Look here. You really are going it at a great pace, you know. Egad, you haven't got an appointment," said Barnacle Junior, as if the thing were growing serious.

"I want to know," said Arthur, and repeated his case.

Barnacle Junior stared at him until his eye-glass fell out, and then put it in again and stared at him until it fell out again. "You have no right to come this sort of move," he then observed with the greatest weakness. "Look here. What do you mean? You told me you didn't know whether it was public business or not?"

"I have now ascertained that it is public business," returned the suitor, "and I want to know" – and again repeated his monotonous inquiry.

Its effect upon young Barnacle was to make him repeat in a defenceless way, "Look here! Upon my SOUL you mustn't come into the place saying you want to know, you know!" The effect of that upon Arthur Clennam was to make him repeat his inquiry in exactly the same words and tone as before. The effect of that upon young Barnacle was to make him a wonderful spectacle of failure and helplessness.

"Well, I tell you what. Look here. You had better try the Secretarial Department," he said at last, sidling to the bell and ringing it. "Jenkinson," to the mashed potatoes messenger, "Mr. Wobbler!"

Arthur Clennam, who now felt that he had devoted himself to the storming of the Circumlocution Office, and must go through with it, accompanied the messenger to another floor of the building, where that functionary pointed out Mr. Wobbler's room. He entered that apartment, and found two gentlemen sitting face to face at a large and easy desk, one of whom was polishing a gunbarrel on his pocket-handkerchief, while the other was spreading marmalade on bread with a paper-knife.

"Mr. Wobbler?" inquired the suitor.

Both gentlemen glanced at him, and seemed surprised at his assurance.

"So he went," said the gentleman with the gun-barrel, who was an extremely deliberate speaker, "down to his cousin's place, and took the Dog with him by rail. Inestimable Dog. Flew at the porter fellow when he was put into the dog-box, and flew at the guard when he was taken out. He got half-a-dozen fellows into a Barn, and a good supply of Rats, and timed the Dog. Finding the Dog able to do it immensely, made the match, and heavily backed the Dog. When the match came off, some devil of a fellow was bought over, Sir, Dog was made drunk, Dog's master was cleaned out."

"Mr. Wobbler?" inquired the suitor.

The gentleman who was spreading the marmalade returned, without looking up from that occupation, "What did he call the Dog?"

"Called him Lovely," said the other gentleman. "Said the Dog was the perfect picture of the old aunt from whom he had expectations. Found him particularly like her when hocussed*."

"Mr. Wobbler?" said the suitor.

Both gentlemen laughed for some time. The gentleman with the gun-barrel, considering it, on inspection, in a satisfactory state, referred it to the other; receiving confirmation of his views, he fitted it into its place in the case before him, and took out the stock and polished that, softly whistling.

"Mr. Wobbler?" said the suitor.

"What's the matter?" then said Mr. Wobbler, with his mouth full.

"I want to know – " and Arthur Clennam again mechanically set forth what he wanted to know.

"Can't inform you," observed Mr. Wobbler, apparently to his lunch. "Never heard of it. Nothing at all to do with it. Better try Mr. Clive, second door on the left in the next passage."

"Perhaps he will give me the same answer."

"Very likely. Don't know anything about it," said Mr. Wobbler.

The suitor turned away and had left the room, when the gentleman with the gun called out "Mister! Hallo!"

He looked in again.

"Shut the door after you. You're letting in a devil of a draught here!"

A few steps brought him to the second door on the left in the next passage. In that room he found three gentlemen; number one doing nothing particular, number two doing nothing particular, number three doing nothing particular. They seemed, however, to be more directly concerned than the others had been in the effective execution of the great principle of the office, as there was an awful inner apartment with a double door, in which the Circumlocution Sages appeared to be assembled in council, and out of which there was an imposing coming of papers, and into which there was an imposing going of papers, almost constantly; wherein another gentleman, number four, was the active instrument.

"I want to know," said Arthur Clennam, – and again stated his case in the same barrel-organ way. As number one referred him to number two, and as number two referred him to number three, he had occasion

* hocussed: made drunk (the reference is still to the dog)

to state it three times before they all referred him to number four, to whom he stated it again.

Number four was a vivacious, well-looking, well-dressed, agreeable young fellow – he was a Barnacle, but on the more sprightly side of the family – and he said in an easy way, "Oh! you had better not bother yourself about it, I think."

"Not bother myself about it?"

"No! I recommend you not to bother yourself about it."

This was such a new point of view that Arthur Clennam found himself at a loss how to receive it.

"You can if you like. I can give you plenty of forms to fill up. Lots of 'em here. You can have a dozen if you like. But you'll never go on with it," said number four.

"Would it be such hopeless work? Excuse me; I am a stranger in England."

"*I* don't say it would be hopeless," returned number four, with a frank smile. "I don't express an opinion about that; I only express an opinion about you. *I* don't think you'd go on with it. However, of course, you can do as you like. I suppose there was a failure in the performance of a contract, or something of that kind, was there?"

"I really don't know."

"Well! That you can find out. Then you'll find out what Department the contract was in, and then you'll find out all about it there."

"I beg your pardon. How shall I find out?"

"Why, you'll – you'll ask till they tell you. Then you'll memorialise that Department (according to regular forms which you'll find out) for leave to memorialise this Department. If you get it (which you may after a time), that memorial must be entered in that Department, sent to be registered in this Department, sent back to be signed by that Department, sent back to be counter-signed by this Department, and then it will begin to be regularly before that Department. You'll find out when the business passes through each of these stages by asking at both Departments till they tell you."

"But surely this is not the way to do the business," Arthur Clennam could not help saying.

This airy young Barnacle was quite entertained by his simplicity in supposing for a moment that it was.

Little Dorrit, *Chapter 10 (Book 1)*

Bran-new people

***Our Mutual Friend** makes a fierce attack on a money-dominated society which has lost touch with proper values. It continues the assault mounted in **Bleak House, Hard Times, Little Dorrit** and **Great Expectations.** The Veneerings and their friends are the yuppies of Victorian England.*

MR. AND MRS. VENEERING were bran-new people in a bran-new house in a bran-new quarter of London. Everything about the Veneerings was spick and span new. All their furniture was new, all their friends were new, all their servants were new, their plate was new, their carriage was new, their harness was new, their horses were new, their pictures were new, they themselves were new, they were as newly married as was lawfully compatible with their having a bran-new baby, and if they had set up a great-grandfather, he would have come home in matting from the Pantechnicon, without a scratch upon him, French polished to the crown of his head.

For, in the Veneering establishment, from the hall-chairs with the new coat of arms, to the grand pianoforte with the new action, and upstairs again to the new fire-escape, all things were in a state of high varnish and polish. And what was observable in the furniture, was observable in the Veneerings – the surface smelt a little too much of the workshop and was a trifle sticky.

There was an innocent piece of dinner-furniture that went upon easy castors and was kept over a livery stable-yard in Duke Street, Saint James's, when not in use, to whom the Veneerings were a source of blind confusion. The name of this article was Twemlow. Being first cousin to Lord Snigsworth, he was in frequent requisition, and at many houses might be said to represent the dining-table in its normal state. Mr. and Mrs. Veneering, for example, arranging a dinner, habitually started with Twemlow, and then put leaves in him, or added guests to him. Sometimes, the table consisted of Twemlow and half a dozen leaves; sometimes, of Twemlow and a dozen leaves; sometimes, Twemlow was pulled out to his utmost extent of twenty leaves. Mr. and Mrs. Veneering on occasions of ceremony faced each other in the centre of the board, and thus the parallel still held; for, it always happened that the more Twemlow was pulled out, the further he found himself from the centre, and the nearer to the sideboard at one end of the room, or the window-curtains at the other.

But, it was not this which steeped the feeble soul of Twemlow in confusion. This he was used to, and could take soundings of. The abyss to which he could find no bottom, and from which started forth the engrossing and ever-swelling difficulty of his life, was the insoluble question whether he was Veneering's oldest friend, or newest friend. To the excogitation of this problem, the harmless gentleman had devoted many anxious hours, both in his lodgings over the livery stable-yard, and in the cold gloom, favourable to meditation, of Saint James's Square. Thus, Twemlow had first known Veneering at his club, where Veneering then knew nobody but the man who made them known to one another, who seemed to be the most intimate friend he had in the world, and whom he had known two days – the bond of union between their souls, the nefarious conduct of the committee respecting the cookery of a fillet of veal, having been accidently cemented at that date. Immediately upon this, Twemlow received an invitation to dine with Veneering, and dined: the man being of the party. Immediately upon that, Twemlow received an invitation to dine with the man, and dined: Veneering being of the party. At the man's were a Member, an Engineer, a Payer-off of the National Debt, a Poem on Shakespeare, a Grievance, and a Public Office, who all seemed to be utter strangers to Veneering. And yet immediately after that, Twemlow received an invitation to dine at Veneerings, expressly to meet the Member, the Engineer, the Payer-off of the National Debt, the Poem on Shakespeare, the Grievance, and the Public Office, and, dining, discovered that all of them were the most intimate friends Veneering had in the world, and that the wives of all of them (who were all there) were the objects of Mrs. Veneering's most devoted affection and tender confidence.

Thus it had come about, that Mr. Twemlow had said to himself in his lodgings, with his hand to his forehead: "I must not think of this. This is enough to soften any man's brain," – and yet was always thinking of it, and could never form a conclusion.

This evening the Veneerings give a banquet. Eleven leaves in the Twemlow; fourteen in company all told. Four pigeon-breasted retainers in plain clothes stand in line in the hall. A fifth retainer, proceeding up the staircase with a mournful air – as who should say, "Here is another wretched creature come to dinner; such is life!" – announces, "Mis-ter Twemlow!"

Mrs. Veneering welcomes her sweet Mr. Twemlow. Mr. Veneering welcomes his dear Twemlow. Mrs. Veneering does not expect that Mr. Twemlow can in nature care much for such insipid things as babies, but so old a friend must please to look at baby. 'Ah! You will know the friend of your family better, Tootleums,' says Mr. Veneering, nodding emotionally at that new article, 'when you begin to take notice.' He then begs to make his dear Twemlow known to his two friends, Mr. Boots and Mr. Brewer – and clearly has no distinct idea which is which.

But now a fearful circumstance occurs.

"Mis-ter and Mis-sis Podsnap!"

"My dear," says Mr. Veneering to Mrs. Veneering, with an air of much friendly interest, while the door stands open, "the Podsnaps."

A too, too smiling large man, with a fatal freshness on him, appearing with his wife, instantly deserts his wife and darts at Twemlow with:

"How do you do? So glad to know you. Charming house you have here. I hope we are not late. So glad of this opportunity, I am sure!"

When the first shock fell upon him, Twemlow twice skipped back in his neat little shoes and his neat little silk stockings of a bygone fashion, as if impelled to leap over a sofa behind him; but the large man closed with him and proved too strong.

"Let me," says the large man, trying to attract the attention of his wife in the distance, "have the pleasure of presenting Mrs. Podsnap to her host. She will be," in his fatal freshness he seems to find perpetual verdure and eternal youth in the phrase, "she will be so glad of the opportunity, I am sure!"

In the meantime, Mrs. Podsnap, unable to originate a mistake on her own account, because Mrs. Veneering is the only other lady there, does her best in the way of handsomely supporting her husband's, by looking towards Mr. Twemlow with a plaintive countenance and remarking to Mrs. Veneering in a feeling manner, firstly, that she fears he has been rather bilious of late, and, secondly, that the baby is already very like him.

It is questionable whether any man quite relishes being mistaken for any other man; but, Mr. Veneering having this very evening set up the shirt-front of the young Antinous* in new worked cambric just come home, is not at all complimented by being supposed to be Twemlow, who is dry and weazen and some thirty years older. Mrs. Veneering equally resents the imputation of being the wife of Twemlow. As to Twemlow, he is so sensible of being a much better bred man than Veneering, that he considers the large man an offensive ass.

In this complicated dilemma, Mr. Veneering approaches the large man with extended hand and, smilingly assures that incorrigible personage that he is delighted to see him: who in his fatal freshness instantly replies:

"Thank you. I am ashamed to say that I cannot at this moment recall where we met, but I am so glad of this opportunity, I am sure!"

* Antinous: a friend of the Roman Emperor Hadrian and famed for his elegance.

Then pouncing upon Twemlow, who holds back with all his feeble might, he is haling him off to present him, as Veneering, to Mrs. Podsnap, when the arrival of more guests unravels the mistake. Whereupon, having re-shaken hands with Veneering as Veneering, he re-shakes hands with Twemlow as Twemlow, and winds it all up to his own perfect satisfaction by saying to the last-named, "Ridiculous opportunity – but so glad of it, I am sure!"

Now, Twemlow having undergone this terrific experience, having likewise noted the fusion of Boots in Brewer and Brewer in Boots, and having further observed that of the remaining seven guests four discreet characters enter with wandering eyes and wholly decline to commit themselves as to which is Veneering, until Veneering has them in his grasp; – Twemlow having profited by these studies, finds his brain wholesomely hardening as he approaches the conclusion that he really is Veneering's oldest friend, when his brain softens again and all is lost, through his eyes encountering Veneering and the large man linked together as twin brothers in the back drawing-room near the conservatory door, and through his ears informing him in the tones of Mrs. Veneering that the same large man is to be baby's godfather.

"Dinner is on the table!"

Thus the melancholy retainer, as who should say, "Come down and be poisoned, ye unhappy children of men!"

Twemlow, having no lady assigned him, goes down in the rear, with his hand to his forehead. Boots and Brewer, thinking him indisposed, whisper, "Man faint. Had no lunch." But he is only stunned by the unvanquishable difficulty of his existence.

Revived by soup, Twemlow discourses mildly of the Court Circular with Boots and Brewer. Is appealed to, at the fish stage of the banquet, by Veneering, on the disputed question whether his cousin Lord Snigsworth is in or out of town? Gives it that his cousin is out of town. "At Snigsworthy Park?" Veneering inquires. "At Snigsworthy," Twemlow rejoins. Boots and Brewer regard this as a man to be cultivated; and Veneering is clear that he is a remunerative article. Meantime the retainer goes round, like a gloomy Analytical Chemist: always seeming to say, after "Chablis, sir?" –"You wouldn't if you knew what it's made of."

The great looking-glass above the sideboard, reflects the table and the company. Reflects the new Veneering crest, in gold and eke in silver, frosted and also thawed, a camel of all work. The Heralds' College found out a Crusading ancestor for Veneering who bore a camel on his shield (or might have done it if he had thought of it), and a caravan of camels take charge of the fruits and flowers and candles, and kneel down to be loaded with the salt. Reflects Veneering; forty, wavy-haired, dark, tending to corpulence, sly, mysterious, filmy – a kind of sufficiently well-looking veiled-prophet, not prophesying. Reflects Mrs. Veneering; fair, aquiline-nosed and fingered, not so much light hair as she might have, gorgeous in raiment and jewels, enthusiastic, propitiatory, conscious that a corner of her husband's veil is over herself. Reflects Podsnap; prosperously feeding, two little light-coloured wiry wings, one on either side of his else bald head, looking as like his hairbrushes as his hair, dissolving view of red beads on his forehead, large allowance of crumpled shirt-collar up behind. Reflects Mrs. Podsnap; fine woman for Professor Owen*, quantity of bone, neck and nostrils like a rocking-horse, hard features, majestic head-dress in which Podsnap has hung golden offerings. Reflects Twemlow; grey, dry, polite, susceptible to east wind, First-Gentleman-in-Europe collar and cravat, cheeks drawn in as if he had made a great effort to retire into himself some years ago, and had got so far and had never got any farther. Reflects mature young lady; raven locks, and complexion that lights up well when well powdered – as it is – carrying on considerably in the captivation of mature young gentleman; with too much nose in his face, too much ginger in his whiskers, too much torso in his waistcoat, too much sparkle in his studs, his eyes, his buttons, his talk, and his teeth. Reflects charming old Lady Tippins on Veneering's right; with an immense obtuse drab oblong face, like a face in a tablespoon, and a dyed Long Walk up the top of her head, as a convenient public approach to the bunch of false hair behind, pleased to patronise Mrs. Veneering opposite, who is pleased to be patronised. Reflects a certain "Mortimer", another of Veneering's oldest friends; who never was in the house before, and appears not to want to come again, who sits disconsolate on Mrs. Veneering's left, and who was inveigled by Lady Tippins (a friend of his boyhood) to come to these people's and talk, and who won't talk. Reflects Eugene, friend of Mortimer; buried alive in the back of his chair, behind a shoulder – with a powder-epaulette on it – of the mature young lady, and gloomily resorting to the champagne chalice whenever proffered by the Analytical Chemist. Lastly, the looking-glass reflects Boots and Brewer, and two other stuffed Buffers interposed between the rest of the company and possible accidents.

The Veneering dinners are excellent dinners – or new people wouldn't come – and all goes well. Notably, Lady Tippins has made a series of experiments on her digestive functions, so extremely complicated and daring, that if they could be published with their results it might benefit the human race.

Our Mutual Friend, *Chapter 2*

* Professor Owen: ran the Natural History Section of the British Museum and specialised in extinct animals.

A love tangle

Tracy Tupman is the romantic in Mr. Pickwick's circle but here the path of true love certainly does not run smooth because of a very fat boy and a snake-in-the-grass in the person of the failed strolling player but successful confidence trickster, Mr. Jingle.

"OH, RACHAEL! say you love me."

"Mr. Tupman," said the spinster aunt, with averted head – "I can hardly speak the words; but – but – you are not wholly indifferent to me."

Mr. Tupman no sooner heard this avowal, than he proceeded to do what his enthusiastic emotions prompted, and what, for aught we know (for we are but little acquainted with such matters), people so circumstanced always do. He jumped up, and, throwing his arm round the neck of the spinster aunt, imprinted upon her lips numerous kisses, which after a due show of struggling and resistance, she received so passively, that there is no telling how many more Mr. Tupman might have bestowed, if the lady had not given a very unaffected start and exclaimed in an affrighted tone –

"Mr. Tupman, we are observed! – we are discovered!"

Mr. Tupman looked round. There was the fat boy, perfectly motionless, with his large circular eyes staring into the arbour, but without the slightest expression on his face that the most expert physiognomist could have referred to astonishment, curiosity, or any other known passion that agitates the human breast. Mr. Tupman gazed on the fat boy, and the fat boy stared at him; and the longer Mr. Tupman observed the utter vacancy of the fat boy's countenance, the more convinced he became that he either did not know, or did not understand, anything that had been going forward. Under this impression, he said with great firmness –

"What do you want here, sir?"

"Supper's ready, sir," was the prompt reply.

"Have you just come here, sir?" inquired Mr. Tupman, with a piercing look.

"Just," replied the fat boy.

Mr. Tupman looked at him very hard again; but there was not a wink in his eye, or a curve in his face.

The fat boy awake

Mr. Tupman took the arm of the spinster aunt, and walked towards the house; the fat boy followed behind.

"He knows nothing of what has happened," he whispered.

"Nothing," said the spinster aunt.

There was a sound behind them, as of an imperfectly suppressed chuckle. Mr. Tupman turned sharply round. No; it could not have been the fat boy; there was not a gleam of mirth, or anything but feeding in his whole visage.

"He must have been fast asleep," whispered Mr. Tupman.

"I have not the least doubt of it," replied the spinster aunt.

They both laughed heartily.

Mr. Tupman was wrong. The fat boy, for once, had not been fast asleep. He was awake – wide awake – to what had been going forward.

It was the old lady's* habit on the fine summer mornings to repair to the arbour in which Mr. Tupman had already signalised himself, in form and manner following: first, the fat boy fetched from a peg behind the old lady's bedroom door, a close black satin bonnet, a warm cotton shawl, and a thick stick with a capacious handle; and the old lady having put on the bonnet and shawl at her leisure, would lean one hand on the stick and the other on the fat boy's shoulder, and walk leisurely to the arbour, where the fat boy would leave her to enjoy the fresh air for the space of half an hour; at the expiration of which time he would return and reconduct her to the house.

The old lady was very precise and very particular; and as this ceremony had been observed for three successive summers without the slightest deviation from the accustomed form, she was not a little surprised on this particular morning, to see the fat boy, instead of leaving the arbour, walk a few paces out of it, look carefully round him in every direction, and return towards her with great stealth and an air of the most profound mystery.

The old lady was timorous – most old ladies are – and her first impression was that the bloated lad was about to do her some grievous bodily harm with the view of possessing himself of her loose coin. She would have cried for assistance, but age and infirmity had long ago deprived her of the power of screaming; she, therefore, watched his motions with feelings of intense terror, which were in no degree diminished by his coming close up to her, and shouting in her ear in an agitated, and as it seemed to her, a threatening tone –

"Missus!"

Now it so happened that Mr. Jingle was walking in the garden close to the arbour at this moment. He too heard the shout of "Missus," and stopped to hear more. There were three reasons for his doing so. In the first place, he was idle and curious; secondly, he was by no means scrupulous; thirdly, and lastly, he was concealed from view by some flowering shrubs. So there he stood, and there he listened.

"Missus!" shouted the fat boy.

"Well, Joe," said the trembling old lady. "I'm sure I have been a good mistress to you, Joe. You have invariably been treated very kindly. You

* the old lady: Mrs. Wardle, mother of Mr. Pickwick's host and of Rachael.

have never had too much to do; and you have always had enough to eat."

This last was an appeal to the fat boy's most sensitive feelings. He seemed touched, as he replied, emphatically –

"I knows I has."

"Then what can you want to do now?" said the old lady, gaining courage.

"I wants to make your flesh creep," replied the boy.

This sounded like a very bloodthirsty mode of showing one's gratitude; and as the old lady did not precisely understand the process by which such a result was to be attained, all her former horrors returned.

"What do you think I see in this very arbour last night?" inquired the boy.

"Bless us! What?" exclaimed the old lady, alarmed at the solemn manner of the corpulent youth.

"The strange gentleman – him as had his arm hurt – a kissin' and huggin' –"

"Who, Joe? None of the servants, I hope."

"Worser than that," roared the fat boy, in the old lady's ear.

"Not one of my grand-da'aters?"

"Worser than that."

"Worse than *that*, Joe!" said the old lady, who had thought this the extreme limit of human atrocity. "Who was it, Joe? I insist upon knowing."

The fat boy looked cautiously round, and having concluded his survey, shouted in the old lady's ear:

"Miss Rachael."

"What!" said the old lady, in a shrill tone. "Speak louder."

"Miss Rachael," roared the fat boy.

"My da'ater!"

The train of nods which the fat boy gave by way of assent, communicated a *blanc-mange* like motion to his fat cheeks.

"And she suffered him!" exclaimed the old lady.

A grin stole over the fat boy's features as he said:

"I see her a kissin' of him agin."

If Mr. Jingle, from his place of concealment, could have beheld the expression which the old lady's face assumed at this communication, the probability is that a sudden burst of laughter would have betrayed his close vicinity to the summer-house. He listened attentively. Fragments of angry sentences such as, "Without my permission!" – "At her time of life" – "Miserable old 'ooman like me" – "Might have waited till I was dead," and so forth, reached his ears; and then he heard the heels of the fat boy's boots crunching the gravel, as he retired and left the old lady alone.

It was a remarkable coincidence perhaps, but it was nevertheless a fact, that Mr. Jingle within five minutes after his arrival at Manor Farm on the preceding night, had inwardly resolved to lay siege to the heart of the spinster aunt, without delay. He had observation enough to see that his off-hand manner was by no means disagreeable to the fair object of his attack; and he had more than a strong suspicion that she possessed that most desirable of all requisites, a small independence. The imperative necessity of ousting his rival by some means or other flashed quickly upon him, and he immediately resolved to adopt certain proceedings tending to that end and object, without a moment's delay. Fielding* tells us that man is fire, and woman tow, and the Prince of Darkness sets a light to 'em. Mr. Jingle knew that young men, to spinster aunts, are as lighted gas to gunpowder, and he determined to essay the effect of an explosion without loss of time.

Full of reflections upon this important decision, he crept from his place of concealment, and, under cover of the shrubs before mentioned, approached the house. Fortune seemed determined to favour his design. Mr. Tupman and the rest of the gentlemen left the garden by the side-gate just as he obtained a view of it; and the young ladies, he knew, had walked out alone, soon after breakfast. The coast was clear.

The breakfast-parlour door was partially open. He peeped in. The spinster aunt was knitting. He coughed; she looked up and smiled. Hesitation formed no part of Mr. Alfred Jingle's character. He laid his finger on his lips mysteriously, walked in, and closed the door.

"Miss Wardle," said Mr. Jingle, with affected earnestness, "forgive intrusion – short acquaintance – no time for ceremony – all discovered."

"Sir!" said the spinster aunt, rather astonished by the unexpected apparition and somewhat doubtful of Mr. Jingle's sanity.

"Hush!" said Mr. Jingle, in a stage whisper; – "large boy – dumpling face – round eyes – rascal!" Here he shook his head expressively, and the spinster aunt trembled with agitation.

"I presume you allude to Joseph, sir?" said the lady, making an effort to appear composed.

"Yes, ma'am – damn that Joe! – treacherous dog, Joe – told the old lady – old lady furious – wild – raving – arbour – Tupman – kissing and hugging – all that sort of thing – eh, ma'am – eh?"

"Mr. Jingle," said the spinster aunt, "if you come here, sir, to insult me –"

"Not at all – by no means," replied the unabashed Mr. Jingle; – "overheard the tale – came to warn you of your danger – tender my

* Fielding: Henry Fielding, eighteenth century author of *Tom Jones*, one of Dickens's favourite novels.

services – prevent the hubbub. Never mind – think it an insult – leave the room" – and he turned, as if to carry the threat into execution.

"What *shall* I do!" said the poor spinster, bursting into tears. "My brother will be furious."

"Of course he will," said Mr. Jingle, pausing – "outrageous."

"Oh, Mr. Jingle, what *can* I say!" exclaimed the spinster aunt, in another flood of despair.

"Say he dreamt it," replied Mr. Jingle, coolly.

A ray of comfort darted across the mind of the spinster aunt at this suggestion. Mr. Jingle perceived it, and followed up his advantage.

"Pooh, pooh! – nothing more easy – blackguard boy – lovely woman – fat boy horsewhipped – you believed – end of the matter – all comfortable."

Whether the probability of escaping from the consequences of this ill-timed discovery was delightful to the spinster's feelings, or whether the hearing herself described as a "lovely woman" softened the asperity of her grief, we know not. She blushed slightly, and cast a grateful look on Mr. Jingle.

That insinuating gentleman sighed deeply, fixed his eyes on the spinster aunt's face for a couple of minutes, started melodramatically, and suddenly withdrew them.

"You seem unhappy, Mr. Jingle," said the lady, in a plaintive voice. "May I show my gratitude for your kind interference, by inquiring into the cause, with a view, if possible, to its removal?"

"Ha!" exclaimed Mr. Jingle, with another start – "removal! remove *my* unhappiness, and your love bestowed upon a man who is insensible to the blessing – who even now contemplates a design upon the affections of the niece of the creature who – but no; he is my friend; I will not expose his vices. Miss Wardle – farewell!" At the conclusion of this address, the most consecutive he was ever known to utter, Mr. Jingle applied to his eyes the remnant of a handkerchief before noticed, and turned towards the door.

"Stay, Mr. Jingle!" said the spinster aunt emphatically. "You have made an allusion to Mr. Tupman – explain it."

"Never!" exclaimed Jingle, with a professional (i.e. theatrical) air. "Never!" and, by way of showing that he had no desire to be questioned further, he drew a chair close to that of the spinster aunt and sat down.

"Mr. Jingle," said the aunt, "I entreat – I implore you, if there is any dreadful mystery connected with Mr. Tupman, reveal it."

"Can I," said Mr. Jingle, fixing his eyes on the aunt's face – "can I see – lovely creature – sacrificed at the shrine – heartless avarice!" He appeared to be struggling with various conflicting emotions for a few seconds, and then said in a low deep voice –

"Tupman only wants your money."

"The wretch!" exclaimed the spinster, with energetic indignation. (Mr. Jingle's doubts were resolved. She *had* money.)

"More than that," said Jingle – "loves another."

"Another!" ejaculated the spinster. "Who?"

"Short girl – black eyes – niece Emily."

There was a pause.

Now, if there were one individual in the whole world, of whom the spinster aunt entertained a mortal and deeply-rooted jealousy, it was this identical niece. The colour rushed over her face and neck, and she tossed her head in silence with an air of ineffable contempt. At last, biting her thin lips, and bridling up, she said –

"It can't be. I won't believe it."

"Watch 'em," said Jingle.

"I will," said the aunt.

"Watch his looks."

"I will."

"His whispers."

"I will."

"He'll sit next her at table."

"Let him."

"He'll flatter her."

"Let him."

"He'll pay her every possible attention."

"Let him."

"And he'll cut you."

"Cut *me*!" screamed the spinster aunt. "*He* cut *me*; – *will* he!" and she trembled with rage and disappointment.

"You will convince yourself?" said Jingle.

"I will."

"You'll show your spirit?"

"I will."

"You'll not have him afterwards?"

"Never."

"You'll take somebody else?"

"Yes."

"You shall."

Mr. Jingle fell on his knees, remained thereupon for five minutes thereafter: and rose the accepted lover of the spinster aunt: conditionally upon Mr. Tupman's perjury being made clear and manifest.

The burden of proof lay with Mr. Alfred Jingle; and he produced his evidence that very day at dinner. The spinster aunt could hardly believe her eyes. Mr. Tracy Tupman was established at Emily's side, ogling, whispering, and smiling, in opposition to Mr. Snodgrass. Not a word, not a look, not a glance, did he bestow upon his heart's pride of the evening before.

"Damn that boy!" thought old Mr. Wardle to himself. – He had heard the story from his mother. "Damn that boy! He *must* have been asleep. It's all imagination."

"Traitor!" thought the spinster aunt. "Dear Mr. Jingle was not deceiving me. Ugh! how I hate the wretch!"

The following conversation may serve to explain to our readers this apparently unaccountable alteration of deportment on the part of Mr. Tracy Tupman.

The time was evening; the scene the garden. There were two figures walking in a side path; one was rather short and stout; the other rather tall and slim. They were Mr. Tupman and Mr. Jingle. The stout figure commenced the dialogue.

"How did I do it?" he inquired.

"Splendid – capital – couldn't act better myself – you must repeat the part tomorrow – every evening, till further notice."

"Does Rachael still wish it?"

"Of course – she don't like it – but must be done – avert suspicion – afraid of her brother – says there's no help for it – only a few days more – when old folks blinded – crown your happiness."

"Any message?"

"Love – best love – kindest regards – unalterable affection. Can I say anything for you?"

"My dear fellow," replied the unsuspicious Mr. Tupman, fervently grasping his "friend's" hand – "carry my best love – say how hard I find it to dissemble – say anything that's kind; but add how sensible I am of the necessity of the suggestion she made to me, through you, this morning. Say I applaud her wisdom and admire her discretion."

"I will. Anything more?"

"Nothing; only add how ardently I long for the time when I may call her mine, and all dissimulation may be unnecessary."

"Certainly, certainly. Anything more?"

"Oh, my friend!" said poor Mr. Tupman, again grasping the hand of his companion, "receive my warmest thanks for your disinterested kindness; and forgive me if I have ever, even in thought, done you the injustice of supposing that you *could* stand in my way. My dear friend, can I ever repay you?"

"Don't talk of it," replied Mr. Jingle. He stopped short, as if suddenly recollecting something, and said – "By-the-bye – can't spare ten pounds, can you?"

The Pickwick Papers, *Chapter 8*

Meet the Dodger

The workhouse orphan, Oliver Twist, has been apprenticed to an undertaker but is unhappy and runs away to London. He is picked off the streets by the Artful Dodger, one of the young gang of thieves organised by Fagin who fences stolen goods. Oliver is too innocent to know he is being recruited.

"Hullo, my covey! What's the row?"

The boy who addressed this inquiry to the young wayfarer, was about his own age, but one of the queerest-looking boys that Oliver had ever seen. He was a snub-nosed, flat-browed, common-faced boy enough; and as dirty a juvenile as one would wish to see; but he had about him all the airs and manners of a man. He was short of his age, with rather bow-legs, and little, sharp, ugly eyes. His hat was stuck on the top of his head so lightly, that it threatened to fall off every moment – and would have done so, very often, if the wearer had not had a knack of every now and then giving his head a sudden twitch, which brought it back to its old place again. He wore a man's coat, which reached nearly to his heels. He had turned the cuffs back, half-way up his arm, to get his hands out of the sleeves: apparently with the ultimate view of thrusting them into the pockets of his corduroy trousers; for there he kept them. He was, altogether, as roystering and swaggering a young gentleman as ever stood four feet six, or something less, in his bluchers.*

"Hullo, my covey! What's the row?" said this strange young gentleman to Oliver.

"I am very hungry and tired," replied Oliver, the tears standing in his eyes as he spoke. "I have walked a long way. I have been walking these seven days."

"Walking for sivin days!" said the young gentleman. "Oh, I see. Beak's order, eh? But," he added, noticing Oliver's look of surprise, "I suppose you don't know what a beak is, my flash com-pan-i-on?"

Oliver mildly replied, that he had always heard a bird's mouth described by the term in question.

"My eyes, how green!" exclaimed the young gentleman. "Why, a beak's a madgst'rate: and when you walk by a beak's order, it's not straightforerd, but always a going up, and nivir a coming down agin.,

* bluchers: leather half-boots

The artful Dodger

Was you never on the mill?"

"What mill?" inquired Oliver.

"What mill! Why, *the mill* – the mill as takes up so little room that it'll work inside a Stone Jug*; and always goes better when the wind's low with people, than when it's high; acos then they can't get workmen. But come," said the young gentleman; "you want grub, and you shall have it. I'm at low-water-mark myself – only one bob and a magpie*, but *as*

* mill . . . Stone Jug: treadmill in a prison

* one bob and a magpie: a shilling and a halfpenny

far *as* it goes, I'll fork out and stump. Up with you on your pins. There! Now then! Morrice!"*

Assisting Oliver to rise, the young gentleman took him to an adjacent chandler's shop, where he purchased a sufficiency of ready-dressed ham and a half-quartern loaf, or, as he himself expressed it, "a fourpenny bran!" the ham being kept clean and preserved from dust, by the ingenious expedient of making a hole in the loaf by pulling out a portion of the crumb, and stuffing it therein. Taking the bread under his arm, the young gentleman turned into a small public-house, and led the way to a tap-room in the rear of the premises. Here, a pot of beer was brought in, by direction of the mysterious youth; and Oliver, falling to, at his new friend's bidding, made a long and hearty meal, during the progress of which, the strange boy eyed him from time to time with great attention.

"Going to London?" said the strange boy, when Oliver had at length concluded.

"Yes."

"Got any lodgings?"

"No."

"Money?"

"No."

The strange boy whistled; and put his arms into his pockets, as far as the big coat-sleeves would let them go.

"Do you live in London?" inquired Oliver.

"Yes. I do, when I'm at home," replied the boy. "I suppose you want some place to sleep in tonight, don't you?"

"I do, indeed," answered Oliver. "I have not slept under a roof since I left the country."

"Don't fret your eyelids on that score," said the young gentleman. "I've got to be in London tonight; and I know a 'spectable old genelman as lives there, wot'll give you lodgings for nothink, and never ask for the change – that is, if any genelman he knows interduces you. And don't he know me? Oh, no! Not in the least! By no means. Certainly not!"

The young gentleman smiled, as if to intimate that the latter fragments of discourse were playfully ironical; and finished the beer as he did so.

This unexpected offer of shelter was too tempting to be resisted; especially as it was immediately followed up, by the assurance that the old gentleman referred to, would doubtless provide Oliver with a comfortable place, without loss of time. This led to a more friendly and confidential dialogue; from which Oliver discovered that his friend's name was Jack Dawkins, and that he was a peculiar pet and *protégé* of the elderly gentleman before mentioned.

* Morrice: slang for "Let's move"

Mr. Dawkins's appearance did not say a vast deal in favour of the comforts which his patron's interest obtained for those whom he took under his protection; but, as he had a rather flighty and dissolute mode of conversing, and furthermore avowed that among his intimate friends he was better known by the *sobriquet** of 'The artful Dodger', Oliver concluded that, being of a dissipated and careless turn, the moral precepts of his benefactor had hitherto been thrown away upon him. Under this impression, he secretly resolved to cultivate the good opinion of the old gentleman as quickly as possible; and, if he found the Dodger incorrigible, as he more than half suspected he should, to decline the honour of his further acquaintance.

Oliver Twist, *Chapter 8*

* *sobriquet*: nickname

The Micawbers

David has been lodging with Mr. and Mrs. Micawber while he is in London and working at a blacking factory, as Dickens himself did.

Though David is still a child the Micawbers treat him as an equal and confide in him about their financial difficulties which are frequent. Mr. Micawber is constantly being arrested for debt and yet is always confident of something "turning up". Mr. Micawber is closely based on Dickens's own father who was also arrested for debt during Dickens's childhood.

"ON SUCH an occasion I will give you, Master Copperfield," said Mrs. Micawber, "in a little more flip*," for we had been having some already, "the memory of my papa and mama."

"Are they dead, ma'am?" I inquired, after drinking the toast in a wine-glass.

"My mama departed this life," said Mrs. Micawber, "before Mr. Micawber's difficulties commenced, or at least before they became pressing. My papa lived to bail Mr. Micawber several times, and then expired, regretted by a numerous circle."

Mrs. Micawber shook her head, and dropped a pious tear upon the twin who happened to be in hand.

As I could hardly hope for a more favourable opportunity of putting a question in which I had a near interest, I said to Mrs. Micawber:

"May I ask, ma'am, what you and Mr. Micawber intend to do, now that Mr. Micawber is out of his difficulties, and at liberty? Have you settled yet?"

"My family," said Mrs. Micawber, who always said those two words with an air, though I never could discover who came under the denomination, "my family are of opinion that Mr. Micawber should quit London, and exert his talents in the country. Mr. Micawber is a man of great talent, Master Copperfield."

I said I was sure of that.

"Of great talent," repeated Mrs. Micawber. "My family are of opinion, that, with a little interest, something might be done for a man of

* flip: a sweetened and spiced mixture of beer and spirits, heated with a poker.

his ability in the Custom House. The influence of my family being local, it is their wish that Mr. Micawber should go down to Plymouth. They think it indispensable that he should be upon the spot."

"That he may be ready?" I suggested.

"Exactly," returned Mrs. Micawber. "That he may be ready – in case of anything turning up."

"And do you go too, ma'am?"

The events of the day, in combination with the twins, if not with the flip, had made Mrs. Micawber hysterical, and she shed tears as she replied:

"I never will desert Mr. Micawber. Mr. Micawber may have concealed his difficulties from me in the first instance, but his sanguine temper may have led him to expect that he would overcome them. The pearl necklace and bracelets which I inherited from mama, have been disposed of for less than half their value; and the set of coral, which was the wedding gift of my papa, has been actually thrown away for nothing. But I never will desert Mr. Micawber. No!" cried Mrs. Micawber, more affected than before, "I never will do it! It's of no use asking me!"

I felt quite uncomfortable – as if Mrs. Micawber supposed I had asked her to do anything of the sort – and sat looking at her in alarm.

"Mr. Micawber has his faults. I do not deny that he is improvident. I do not deny that he has kept me in the dark as to his resources and his liabilities both," she went on, looking at the wall; "but I never will desert Mr. Micawber!"

Mrs. Micawber having now raised her voice into a perfect scream, I was so frightened that I ran off to the club-room, and disturbed Mr. Micawber in the act of presiding at a long table, and leading the chorus of

Gee up, Dobbin,
Gee ho, Dobbin,
Gee up, Dobbin,
Gee up, and gee ho – o – o!

– with the tidings that Mrs. Micawber was in an alarming state, upon which he immediately burst into tears, and came away with me with his waistcoat full of the heads and tails of shrimps, of which he had been partaking.

"Emma, my angel!" cried Mr. Micawber, running into the room; "what is the matter?"

"I never will desert you, Micawber!" she exclaimed.

"My life!" said Mr. Micawber, taking her in his arms. "I am perfectly aware of it."

Mr. Micawber delivers some valedictory remarks

"He is the parent of my children! He is the father of my twins! He is the husband of my affections," cried Mrs. Micawber, struggling; "and I ne – ver – will – desert Mr. Micawber!"

Mr. Micawber was so deeply affected by this proof of her devotion (as to me, I was dissolved in tears), that he hung over her in a passionate manner, imploring her to look up, and to be calm. But the more he asked Mrs. Micawber to look up, the more she fixed her eyes on nothing; and the more he asked her to compose herself, the more she wouldn't. Consequently Mr. Micawber was soon so overcome, that he mingled his tears with hers and mine; until he begged me to do him the favour of taking a chair on the staircase, while he got her into bed. I would have taken my leave for the night, but he would not hear of my doing that until the strangers' bell should ring. So I sat at the staircase window, until he came out with another chair and joined me.

"How is Mrs. Micawber now, sir?" I said.

"Very low," said Mr. Micawber, shaking his head; "reaction. Ah, this has been a dreadful day! We stand alone now – everything is gone from us!"

Mr. Micawber pressed my hand, and groaned, and afterwards shed tears. I was greatly touched, and disappointed too, for I had expected that we should be quite gay on this happy and long-looked-for occasion. But Mr. and Mrs. Micawber were so used to their old difficulties, I think, that they felt quite shipwrecked when they came to consider that they were released from them. All their elasticity was departed, and I never saw them half so wretched as on this night; insomuch that when the bell rang, and Mr. Micawber walked with me to the lodge, and parted from me there with a blessing, I felt quite afraid to leave him by himself, he was so profoundly miserable.

But through all the confusion and lowness of spirits in which we had been, so unexpectedly to me, involved, I plainly discerned that Mr. and Mrs. Micawber and their family were going away from London, and that a parting between us was near at hand.

I passed my evenings with Mr. and Mrs. Micawber, during the remaining term of our residence under the same roof; and I think we became fonder of one another as the time went on. On the last Sunday, they invited me to dinner; and we had a loin of pork and apple sauce, and a pudding. I had bought a spotted wooden horse over-night as a parting gift to little Wilkins Micawber – that was the boy – and a doll for little Emma. I had also bestowed a shilling on the Orfling,* who was about to be disbanded.

We had a very pleasant day, though we were all in a tender state about our approaching separation.

"I shall never, Master Copperfield," said Mrs. Micawber, "revert to the period when Mr. Micawber was in difficulties, without thinking of you. Your conduct has always been of the most delicate and obliging description. You have never been a lodger. You have been a friend."

"My dear," said Mr. Micawber; "Copperfield," for so he had been accustomed to call me, of late, "has a heart to feel for the distresses of his fellow-creatures when they are behind a cloud, and a head to plan, and a hand to – in short, a general ability to dispose of such available property as could be made away with."

I expressed my sense of this commendation, and said I was very sorry we were going to lose one another.

"My dear young friend," said Mr. Micawber, "I am older than you; a man of some experience in life, and – and of some experience, in short, in difficulties, generally speaking. At present, and until something turns up (which I am, I may say, hourly expecting), I have nothing to bestow but advice. Still my advice is so far worth taking, that – in short, that I have never taken it myself, and am the" – here Mr. Micawber, who had been

* Orfling: Mrs. Micawber's maid who told David she was an "Orfling" (i.e. orphan) from a workhouse.

beaming and smiling, all over his head and face, up to the present moment, checked himself and frowned – "the miserable wretch you behold."

"My dear Micawber!" urged his wife.

"I say," returned Mr. Micawber, quite forgetting himself, and smiling again, "the miserable wretch you behold. My advice is, never do tomorrow what you can do today. Procrastination is the thief of time. Collar him!"

"My poor papa's maxim," Mrs. Micawber observed.

"My dear," said Mr. Micawber, "your papa was very well in his way, and Heaven forbid that I should disparage him. Take him for all in all, we ne'er shall – in short, make the acquaintance, probably, of anybody else possessing, at his time of life, the same legs for gaiters, and able to read the same description of print, without spectacles. But he applied that maxim to our marriage, my dear; and that was so far prematurely entered into, in consequence, that I never recovered the expense."

Mr. Micawber looked aside at Mrs. Micawber, and added: "Not that I am sorry for it. Quite the contrary, my love." After which, he was grave for a minute or so.

"My other piece of advice, Copperfield," said Mr. Micawber, "you know. Annual income twenty pounds, annual expenditure nineteen nineteen and six, result happiness. Annual income twenty pounds, annual expenditure twenty pounds ought and six, result misery. The blossom is blighted, the leaf is withered, the god of day goes down upon the dreary scene, and – and in short you are for ever floored. As I am!"

To make his example the more impressive, Mr. Micawber drank a glass of punch with an air of great enjoyment and satisfaction, and whistled the College Hornpipe.

I did not fail to assure him that I would store these precepts in my mind, though indeed I had no need to do so, for, at the time, they affected me visibly. Next morning I met the whole family at the coach office, and saw them, with a desolate heart, take their places outside, at the back.

"Master Copperfield," said Mrs. Micawber, "God bless you! I never can forget all that, you know, and I never would if I could."

"Copperfield," said Mr. Micawber, "farewell! Every happiness and prosperity! If, in the progress of revolving years, I could persuade myself that my blighted destiny had been a warning to you, I should feel that I had not occupied another man's place in existence altogether in vain. In case of anything turning up (of which I am rather confident), I shall be extremely happy if it should be in my power to improve your prospects."

David Copperfield, *Chapter12*

Wegg and Boffin

Silas Wegg is an unscrupulous street trader with a wooden leg and it is typical of Dickens that this leg becomes more and more expressive of Wegg's character. Mr. Boffin whom he meets for the first time in the passage, is illiterate but rich. He has made a fortune out of London's dust heaps and is known as the Golden Dustman. Boffin hires Wegg to read to him.

OVER AGAINST a London house, a corner house not far from Cavendish Square, a man with a wooden leg had sat for some years, with his remaining foot in a basket in cold weather, picking up a living on this wise: – Every morning at eight o'clock, he stumped to the corner, carrying a chair, a clothes-horse, a pair of trestles, a board, a basket, and an umbrella, all strapped together. Separating these, the board and trestles became a counter, the basket supplied the few small lots of fruit and sweets that he offered for sale upon it and became a foot-warmer, the unfolded clothes-horse displayed a choice collection of half-penny ballads and became a screen, and the stool planted within it became his post for the rest of the day. All weathers saw the man at the post. This is to be accepted in a double sense, for he contrived a back to his wooden stool, by placing it against the lamp-post. When the weather was wet, he put up his umbrella over his stock in trade, not over himself; when the weather was dry, he furled that faded article, tied it round with a piece of yarn, and laid it cross-wise under the trestles: where it looked like an unwholesomely-forced lettuce that had lost in colour and crispness what it had gained in size.

He had established his right to the corner, by imperceptible prescription. He had never varied his ground an inch, but had in the beginning diffidently taken the corner upon which the side of the house gave. A howling corner in the winter time, a dusty corner in the summer time, an undesirable corner at the best of times. Shelterless fragments of straw and paper got up revolving storms there, when the main street was at peace; and the water-cart, as if it were drunk or short-sighted, came blundering and jolting round it, making it muddy when all else was clean.

Street scavenging

On the front of his sale-board hung a little placard, like a kettle-holder, bearing the inscription in his own small text:

Errands gone
On with fi
Delity By
Ladies and Gentlemen
I remain
Your humble Servt:
Silas Wegg

He had not only settled it with himself in course of time, that he was errand-goer by appointment to the house at the corner (though he received such commissions not half-a-dozen times in a year, and then only as some servant's deputy), but also that he was one of the house's retainers and owed vassalage to it and was bound to leal and loyal interest in it. For this reason, he always spoke of it as "Our House", and, though his knowledge of its affairs was mostly speculative and all wrong, claimed to be in its confidence. On similar grounds he never beheld an inmate at any one of its windows but he touched his hat. Yet, he knew so little about the inmates that he gave them names of his own invention: as "Miss Elizabeth", "Master George", "Aunt Jane", "Uncle Parker" – having no authority whatever for any such designations, but particularly the last – to which, as a natural consequence, he stuck with great obstinacy.

Over the house itself, he exercised the same imaginary power as over its inhabitants and their affairs. He had never been in it, the length of a piece of fat black water-pipe which trailed itself over the area-door into a damp stone passage, and had rather the air of a leech on the house that had "taken" wonderfully; but this was no impediment to his arranging it according to a plan of his own. It was a great dingy house with a quantity of dim side window and blank back premises, and it cost his mind a world of trouble so to lay it out as to account for everything in its external appearance. But, this once done, was quite satisfactory, and he rested persuaded, that he knew his way about the house blindfold: from the barred garrets in the high roof, to the two iron extinguishers before the main door – which seemed to request all lively visitors to have the kindness to put themselves out, before entering.

Assuredly, this stall of Silas Wegg's was the hardest little stall of all the sterile little stalls in London. It gave you the face-ache to look at his apples, the stomach-ache to look at his oranges, the tooth-ache to look at his nuts. Of the latter commodity he had always a grim little heap, on which lay a little wooden measure which had no discernible inside, and was considered to represent the penn'orth appointed by Magna Charta. Whether from too much east wind or no – it was an easterly corner – the stall, the stock, and the keeper, were all as dry as the Desert. Wegg was a knotty man, and a close-grained, with a face carved out of very hard material, that had just as much play of expression as a watchman's rattle. When he laughed, certain jerks occurred in it, and the rattle sprung. Sooth to say, he was so wooden a man that he seemed to have taken his wooden leg naturally, and rather suggested to the fanciful observer, that he might be expected – if his development received no untimely check – to be completely set up with a pair of wooden legs in about six months.

Mr. Wegg was an observant person, or, as he himself said, "took a powerful sight of notice". He saluted all his regular passers-by every day, as he sat on his stool backed up by the lamp-post; and on the adaptable character of these salutes he greatly plumed himself. Thus, to the rector, he addressed a bow, compounded of lay deference, and a slight touch of the shady preliminary meditation at church; to the doctor, a confidential bow, as to a gentleman whose acquaintance with his inside he begged respectfully to acknowledge; before the Quality he delighted to abase himself, and for Uncle Parker, who was in the army (at least, so he had settled it), he put his open hand to the side of his hat, in a military manner which that angry-eyed buttoned-up inflammatory-faced old gentleman appeared but imperfectly to appreciate.

The only article in which Silas dealt, that was not hard, was gingerbread. On a certain day, some wretched infant having purchased the damp gingerbread-horse (fearfully out of condition), and the adhesive bird-cage, which had been exposed for the day's sale, he had taken a tin box from under his stool to produce a relay of those dreadful specimens, and was going to look in at the lid, when he said to himself, pausing: "Oh! Here you are again!"

The words referred to a broad, round-shouldered, one-sided old fellow in mourning, coming comically ambling towards the corner, dressed in a pea over-coat, and carrying a large stick. He wore thick shoes, and thick leather gaiters, and thick gloves like a hedger's. Both as to his dress and to himself, he was of an overlapping rhinoceros build, with folds in his cheeks, and his forehead, and his eyelids, and his lips, and his ears; but with bright, eager, childishly-inquiring, grey eyes, under his ragged eyebrows, and broad-brimmed hat. A very odd-looking old fellow altogether.

"Here you are again," repeated Mr. Wegg, musing. "And what are you now? Are you in the Funns*, or where are you? Have you lately come to settle in this neighbourhood, or do you own to another neighbourhood? Are you in independent circumstances, or is it wasting the motions of a bow on you? Come! I'll speculate! I'll invest a bow in you."

Which Mr. Wegg, having replaced his tin box, accordingly did, as he rose to bait his gingerbread-trap for some other devoted infant. The salute was acknowledged with:

"Morning, sir! Morning! Morning!"

("Calls me Sir!" said Mr. Wegg, to himself. "*He* won't answer. A bow gone!")

"Morning, morning, morning!"

"Appears to be rather a 'arty old cock, too," said Mr. Wegg, as before.

* Funns: i.e. Funds. Wegg wonders if Boffin is a well-to-do investor.

"Good morning to *you*, sir."

"Do you remember me, then?" asked his new acquaintance, stopping in his amble, one-sided, before the stall, and speaking in a pounding way, though with great good-humour.

"I have noticed you go past our house, sir, several times in the course of the last week or so."

"Our house," repeated the other. "Meaning – ?"

"Yes," said Mr. Wegg, nodding, as the other pointed the clumsy forefinger of his right glove at the corner house.

"Oh! Now, what," pursued the old fellow, in an inquisitive manner, carrying his knotted stick in his left arm as if it were a baby, "what do they allow you now?"

"It's job work that I do for our house," returned Silas, drily, and with reticence; "it's not yet brought to an exact allowance."

"Oh! It's not yet brought to an exact allowance? No! It's not yet brought to an exact allowance. Oh! – Morning, morning, morning!"

"Appears to be rather a cracked old cock," thought Silas, qualifying his former good opinion, as the other ambled off. But, in a moment he was back again with the question:

"How did you get your wooden leg?"

Mr. Wegg replied, (tartly to this personal inquiry), "In an accident."

"Do you like it?"

"Well! I haven't got to keep it warm," Mr. Wegg made answer, in a sort of desperation occasioned by the singularity of the question.

"He hasn't," repeated the other to his knotted stick, as he gave it a hug; "he hasn't got – ha! – ha! – to keep it warm! Did you ever hear of the name of Boffin?"

"No," said Mr. Wegg, who was growing restive under this examination. "I never did hear of the name of Boffin."

"Do you like it?"

"Why, no," retorted Mr. Wegg, again approaching desperation; "I can't say I do."

"Why don't you like it?"

"I don't know why I don't," retorted Mr. Wegg, approaching frenzy, "but I don't at all."

"Now, I'll tell you something that'll make you sorry for that," said the stranger, smiling. "My name's Boffin."

"I can't help it!" returned Mr. Wegg. Implying in his manner the offensive addition, "and if I could, I wouldn't."

"But there's another chance for you," said Mr. Boffin, smiling still, "Do you like the name of Nicodemus? Think it over. Nick, or Noddy."

"It is not, sir," Mr. Wegg rejoined, as he sat down on his stool, with an air of gentle resignation, combined with melancholy candour; "it is not a name as I could wish any one that I had a respect for, to call *me* by; but there may be persons that would not view it with the same objections. – I don't know why," Mr. Wegg added, anticipating another question.

"Noddy Boffin," said that gentleman. "Noddy. That's my name. Noddy – or Nick – Boffin. What's your name?"

"Silas Wegg. – I don't," said Mr. Wegg, bestirring himself to take the same precaution as before, "I don't know why Silas, and I don't know why Wegg."

"Now, Wegg," said Mr. Boffin, hugging his stick closer, "I want to make a sort of offer to you. Do you remember when you first see me?"

The wooden Wegg looked at him with a meditative eye, and also with a softened air as descrying possibility of profit. "Let me think. I ain't quite sure, and yet I generally take a powerful sight of notice, too. Was it on a Monday morning, when the butcher-boy had been to our house for orders, and bought a ballad of me, which, being unacquainted with the tune, I run it over to him?"

"Right, Wegg, right! But he bought more than one."

"Yes, to be sure, sir; he bought several; and wishing to lay out his money to the best, he took my opinion to guide his choice, and we went over the collection together. To be sure we did. Here was him as it might be, and here was myself as it might be, and there was you, Mr. Boffin, as you identically are, with your self-same stick under your very same arm, and your very same back towards us. To – be – sure!" added Mr. Wegg, looking a little round Mr. Boffin, to take him in the rear, and identify this last extraordinary coincidence, "your wery self-same back!"

"What do you think I was doing, Wegg?"

"I should judge, sir, that you might be glancing your eye down the street."

"No, Wegg. I was a listening."

"Was you, indeed?" said Mr. Wegg, dubiously.

"Not in a dishonourable way, Wegg, because you was singing to the butcher; and you wouldn't sing secrets to a butcher in the street, you know."

"It never happened that I did so yet, to the best of my remembrance," said Mr. Wegg, cautiously, "But I might do it. A man can't say what he might wish to do some day or another." (This, not to release any little advantage he might derive from Mr. Boffin's avowal.)

"Well," repeated Boffin, "I was a listening to you and to him. And what do you – you haven't got another stool, have you? I'm rather thick in my breath."

"I haven't got another, but you're welcome to this," said Wegg, resigning it. "It's a treat to me to stand."

"Lard!" exclaimed Mr. Boffin, in a tone of great enjoyment, as he settled himself down, still nursing his stick like a baby, "it's a pleasant place, this! And then to be shut in on each side, with these ballads, like so many book-leaf blinkers! Why, it's delightful!"

"If I am not mistaken, sir," Mr. Wegg delicately hinted, resting a hand on his stall, and bending over the discursive Boffin, "you alluded to some offer or another that was in your mind?"

"I'm coming to it! All right. I'm coming to it! I was going to say that when I listened that morning, I listened with hadmiration amounting to haw. I thought to myself, 'Here's a man with a wooden leg – a literary man with –'"

"N – not exactly so, sir," said Mr. Wegg.

"Why, you know every one of these songs by name and by tune, and if you want to read or to sing any one on 'em off straight, you've only to whip on your spectacles and do it!" cried Mr. Boffin. "I see you at it!"

"Well, sir," returned Mr. Wegg, with a conscious inclination of the head; "we'll say literary, then."

"'A literary man – *with* a wooden leg – and all Print is open to him!' That's what I thought to myself, that morning," pursued Mr. Boffin, leaning forward to describe, uncramped by the clothes-horse, as large an arc as his right arm could make; "'all Print is open to him!' And it is, ain't it?"

"Why, truly, sir," Mr. Wegg admitted, with modesty; "I believe you couldn't show me the piece of English print, that I wouldn't be equal to collaring and throwing."

"On the spot?" said Mr. Boffin.

"On the spot."

"I know'd it! Then consider this. Here am I, a man without a wooden leg, and yet all print is shut to me."

"Indeed, sir?" Mr. Wegg returned with increasing self-complacency. "Education neglected?"

"Neg – lected!" repeated Boffin, with emphasis. "That ain't no word for it. I don't mean to say but what if you showed me a B, I could so far give you change for it, as to answer Boffin."

"Come, come, sir," said Mr. Wegg, throwing in a little encouragement, "that's something, too."

"It's something," answered Mr. Boffin, "but I'll take my oath it ain't much."

"Perhaps it's not as much as could be wished by an inquiring mind, sir," Mr. Wegg admitted.

"Now, look here. I'm retired from business. Me and Mrs. Boffin – Henerietty Boffin – which her father's name was Henery, and her mother's name was Hetty, and so you get it – we live on a compittance, under the will of a diseased governor."

"Gentleman dead, sir?"

"Man alive, don't I tell you? A diseased governor? Now, it's too late for me to begin shovelling and sifting at alphabeds and grammar-books. I'm getting to be a old bird, and I want to take it easy. But I want some reading – some fine bold reading, some splendid book in a gorging Lord-Mayor's-Show of wollumes" (probably meaning gorgeous, but misled by association of ideas); "as'll reach right down your pint of view, and take time to go by you. How can I get that reading, Wegg? By," tapping him on the breast with the head of his thick stick, "paying a man truly qualified to do it, so much an hour (say twopence) to come and do it."

"Hem! Flattered, sir, I am sure," said Wegg, beginning to regard himself in quite a new light. "Hew! This is the offer you mentioned, sir?"

"Yes. Do you like it?"

"I am considering of it, Mr. Boffin."

"I don't," said Boffin, in a free-handed manner, "want to tie a literary man – *with* a wooden leg – down too tight. A halfpenny an hour shan't part us. The hours are your own to choose, after you've done for the day with your house here. I live over Maiden-Lane way – out Holloway direction – and you've only got to go East-and-by-North when you've finished here, and you're there. Twopence halfpenny an hour," said Boffin, taking a piece of chalk from his pocket and getting off the stool to work the sum on the top of it in his own way; "two long'uns and a short'un – twopence halfpenny; two short'uns is a long'un and two two long'uns is four long'uns – making five long'uns; six nights a week at five long'uns a night," scoring them all down separately, "and you mount up to thirty long'uns. A round'un! Half-a-crown*!"

Pointing to this result as a large and satisfactory one, Mr. Boffin smeared it out with his moistened glove, and sat down on the remains.

"Half-a-crown," said Wegg, meditating. "Yes. (It ain't much, sir.) Half-a-crown."

"Per week, you know."

"Per week. Yes. As to the amount of strain upon the intellect now. Was you thinking at all of poetry?" Mr. Wegg inquired, musing.

"Would it come dearer?" Mr. Boffin asked.

"It would come dearer," Mr. Wegg returned. "For when a person comes to grind off poetry night after night, it is but right he should expect to be paid for its weakening effect on his mind."

"To tell you the truth Wegg," said Boffin, "I wasn't thinking of poetry, except in so fur as this: – If you was to happen now and then to feel yourself in the mind to tip me and Mrs. Boffin one of your ballads,

* Half-a-crown = two shillings and sixpence ($12\frac{1}{2}$p in modern money)

why then we should drop into poetry."

"I follow you, sir," said Wegg. "But not being a regular musical professional, I should be loath to engage myself for that; and therefore when I dropped into poetry, I should ask to be considered so fur, in the light of a friend."

At this, Mr. Boffin's eyes sparkled, and he shook Silas earnestly by the hand: protesting that it was more than he could have asked, and that he took it very kindly indeed.

"What do you think of the terms, Wegg?" Mr. Boffin then demanded, with unconcealed anxiety.

Silas, who had stimulated this anxiety by his hard reserve of manner, and who had begun to understand his man very well, replied with an air; as if he were saying something extraordinarily generous and great:

"Mr. Boffin, I never bargain."

"So I should have thought of you!" said Mr. Boffin, admiringly.

"No, sir. I never did 'aggle and I never will 'aggle. Consequently I meet you at once, free and fair, with – Done, for double the money!"

Our Mutual Friend, *Chapter 5*

Chez Podsnap

Mr. Podsnap is a complacent and opinionated insurance broker (see page 96), who asserts the rightness of everything English and regards other countries as "a mistake". This passage sees him engaging with a foreign gentleman at a dinner party designed "to clear off all those people who are due".

Hideous solidity was the characteristic of the Podsnap plate. Everything was made to look as heavy as it could, and to take up as much room as possible. Everything said boastfully, "Here you have as much of me in my ugliness as if I were only lead; but I am so many ounces of precious metal worth so much an ounce; – wouldn't you like to melt me down?" A corpulent straddling epergne*, blotched all over as if it had broken out in an eruption rather than been ornamented, delivered this address from an unsightly silver platform in the centre of the table. Four silver wine-coolers, each furnished with four staring heads, each head obtrusively carrying a big silver ring in each of its ears, conveyed the sentiment up and down the table, and handed it on to the pot-bellied silver salt-cellars. All the big silver spoons and forks widened the mouths of the company expressly for the purpose of thrusting the sentiment down their throats with every morsel they ate.

The majority of the guests were like the plate, and included several heavy articles weighing ever so much. But there was a foreign gentleman among them; whom Mr. Podsnap had invited after much debate with himself – believing the whole European continent to be in mortal alliance against the young person – and there was a droll disposition, not only on the part of Mr. Podsnap, but of everybody else, to treat him as if he were a child who was hard of hearing.

As a delicate concession to this unfortunately-born foreigner, Mr. Podsnap, in receiving him, had presented his wife as "Madame Podsnap"; also his daughter as "Mademoiselle Podsnap," with some inclination to add "ma fille*," in which bold venture, however, he checked himself. The Veneerings being at that time the only other arrivals, he had added (in a condescendingly explanatory manner),

* epergne: ornamental centrepiece for a table

* "ma fille": Dickens describes both Mrs. Podsnap and her daughter as "rocking horses" so it is likely that Podsnap would have been meant to mispronounce the French as "filly".

"Monsieur Vey-nair-reeng," and had then subsided into English.

"How Do You Like London?" Mr. Podsnap now inquired from his station of host, as if he were administering something in the nature of a powder or potion to the deaf child; "London, Londres, London?"

The foreign gentleman admired it.

"You find it Very Large?" said Mr. Podsnap, spaciously.

The foreign gentleman found it very large.

"And Very Rich?"

The foreign gentleman found it, without doubt, enormément riche.

"Enormously Rich, We say," returned Mr. Podsnap, in a condescending manner. "Our English adverbs do Not terminate in Mong, and We Pronounce the 'ch' as if it were a 't' before it. We Say Ritch."

"Reetch," remarked the foreign gentleman.

"And Do You Find, Sir," pursued Mr. Podsnap, with dignity, "Many Evidences that Strike You, of our British Constitution in the Streets Of The World's Metropolis, London, Londres, London?"

The foreign gentleman begged to be pardoned, but did not altogether understand.

"The Constitution Britannique," Mr. Podsnap explained, as if he were teaching in an infant school. "We Say British, But You Say Britannique, You Know" (forgivingly, as if that were not his fault). "The Constitution, Sir."

The foreign gentleman said, "Mais, yees; I know eem."

A youngish sallowish gentleman in spectacles, with a lumpy forehead, seated in a supplementary chair at a corner of the table, here caused a profound sensation by saying, in a raised voice, "ESKER," and then stopping dead.

"Mais oui," said the foreign gentleman, turning towards him. "Est-ce-que? Quoi donc?"

But the gentleman with the lumpy forehead having for the time delivered himself of all that he found behind his lumps, spake for the time no more.

"I Was Inquiring," said Mr. Podsnap, resuming the thread of his discourse, "Whether You Have Observed in our Streets as We should say, Upon our Pavvy as You would say, any Tokens –"

The foreign gentleman with patient courtesy entreated pardon; "But what was tokenz?"

"Marks," said Mr. Podsnap; "Signs, you know, Appearances – Traces."

"Ah! Of a Orse?" inquired the foreign gentleman.

"We call it Horse," said Mr. Podsnap, with forbearance. "In England, Angleterr, England, We Aspirate the 'H', and We Say 'Horse'.

Only our Lower Classes Say 'Orse'!"

"Pardon," said the foreign gentleman; "I am alwiz wrong!"

"Our Language," said Mr. Podsnap, with a gracious consciousness of being always right, "is Difficult. Ours is a Copious Language, and Trying to Strangers. I will not Pursue my Question."

But the lumpy gentleman, unwilling to give it up, again madly said, "ESKER," and again spake no more.

"It merely referred," Mr. Podsnap explained, with a sense of meritorious proprietorship, "to Our Constitution, Sir. We Englishmen are Very Proud of our Constitution, Sir. It Was Bestowed Upon Us By Providence. No Other Country is so Favoured as This Country."

"And ozer countries? –" the foreign gentleman was beginning, when Mr. Podsnap put him right again.

"We do not say Ozer; we say Other: the letters are 'T' and 'H'; you say Tay and Aish, You Know" (still with clemency). "The sound is 'th'–'th'!"

"And *other* countries," said the foreign gentleman. "They do how?"

"They do, Sir," returned Mr. Podsnap, gravely shaking his head; "they do – I am sorry to be obliged to say it – *as* they do."

"It was a little particular of Providence," said the foreign gentleman, laughing; "for the frontier is not large."

"Undoubtedly," assented Mr. Podsnap; "But So it is. It was the Charter of the Land. This Island was Blest, Sir, to the Direct Exclusion of such Other Countries as – as there may happen to be. And if we were all Englishmen present, I would say," added Mr. Podsnap, looking round upon his compatriots, and sounding solemnly with his theme, "that there is in the Englishman a combination of qualities, a modesty, an independence, a responsibility, a repose, combined with an absence of everything calculated to call a blush into the cheek of a young person, which one would seek in vain among the Nations of the Earth."

Having delivered this little summary, Mr. Podsnap's face flushed as he thought of the remote possibility of its being at all qualified by any prejudiced citizen of any other country; and, with his favourite right-arm flourish, he put the rest of Europe and the whole of Asia, Africa, and America nowhere.

Our Mutual Friend, *Chapter 11*

Uriah Heep

David encounters one of Dickens's greatest hypocrites, the always 'umble' Uriah Heep.

"Would you like to be taught Latin?" I said, briskly. "I will teach it you with pleasure, as I learn it."

"Oh, thank you, Master Copperfield," he answered, shaking his head, "I am sure it's very kind of you to make the offer, but I am much too umble to accept it."

"What nonsense, Uriah!"

"Oh, indeed you must excuse me, Master Copperfield! I am greatly obliged, and I should like it of all things, I assure you; but I am far too umble. There are people enough to tread upon me in my lowly state, without my doing outrage to their feelings by possessing learning. Learning ain't for me. A person like myself had better not aspire. If he is to get on in life, he must get on umbly, Master Copperfield!"

I never saw his mouth so wide, or the creases in his cheeks so deep, as when he delivered himself of these sentiments: shaking his head all the time, and writhing modestly.

"I think you are wrong, Uriah," I said, "I dare say there are several things that I could teach you, if you would like to learn them."

"Oh, I don't doubt that, Master Copperfield," he answered; "not in the least. But not being umble yourself, you don't judge well, perhaps, for them that are. I won't provoke my betters with knowledge, thank you. I'm much too umble. Here is my umble dwelling, Master Copperfield!"

David Copperfield, *Chapter 17*

Crime and Punishment

"Newgate: Committed for Trial" by Frank Holl (1878)

A visit to Newgate

__Sketches by Boz__ was Dickens's first book and most of the articles in it appeared originally in the paper he worked for as a young man, __The Morning Chronicle__, and in several periodicals.

"A visit to Newgate" was written especially for the collected __Sketches__ in 1836. Dickens's involvement with prisons precedes this visit: his father was imprisoned for debt in the Marshalsea Prison shortly after Charles's twelfth birthday. He seems to have had a life-long interest in the penal system, capital punishment and what we now know as criminology.

THE PRESS-YARD, well known by name to newspaper readers, from its frequent mention in accounts of executions, is at the corner of the building, and next to the ordinary's house, in Newgate-street: running from Newgate-street, towards the centre of the prison, parallel with Newgate-market. It is a long, narrow court, of which a portion of the wall in Newgate-street forms one end, and the gate the other. At the upper end, on the left hand – that is, adjoining the wall in Newgate-street – is a cistern of water, and at the bottom a double grating (of which the gate itself forms a part) similar to that before described. Through these grates the prisoners are allowed to see their friends; a turnkey always remaining in the vacant space between, during the whole interview. Immediately on the right as you enter, is a building containing the press-room, day-room, and cells; the yard is on every side surrounded by lofty walls guarded by *chevaux de frise**; and the whole is under the constant inspection of vigilant and experienced turnkeys.

In the first apartment into which we were conducted – which was at the top of a staircase, and immediately over the press-room – were five-and-twenty or thirty prisoners, all under sentence of death, awaiting the result of the recorder's report – men of all ages and appearances, from a hardened old offender with swarthy face and grizzly beard of three days' growth, to a handsome boy, not fourteen years old, and of singularly youthful appearance even for that age, who had been condemned for burglary. There was nothing remarkable in the appearance of these prisoners. One or two decently dressed men were brooding with a

* *chevaux de frise*: curved iron spikes set on the top of the walls.

Newgate Prison in London

dejected air over the fire; several little groups of two or three had been engaged in conversation at the upper end of the room, or in the windows; and the remainder were crowded round a young man seated at a table, who appeared to be engaged in teaching the younger ones to write. The room was large, airy, and clean. There was very little anxiety or mental suffering depicted in the countenance of any of the men; – they had all been sentenced to death, it is true, and the recorder's report had not yet been made; but, we question whether there was a man among them, notwithstanding, who did not *know* that although he had undergone the ceremony, it never was intended that his life should be sacrificed. On the table lay a Testament, but there were no tokens of its having been in recent use.

In the press-room below, were three men, the nature of whose offence rendered it necessary to separate them, even from their companions in guilt. It is a long, sombre room, with two windows sunk into the stone wall, and here the wretched men are pinioned on the morning of their execution, before moving towards the scaffold. The fate of one of these prisoners was uncertain; some mitigatory circumstances having come to light since his trial, which had been humanely represented in the proper quarter. The other two had nothing to expect from the mercy of the crown; their doom was sealed; no plea could be urged in extenuation of their crime, and they well knew that for them there was no hope in this world. "The two short ones," the turnkey whispered, "were dead men."

The man to whom we have alluded as entertaining some hopes of escape, was lounging, at the greatest distance he could place between himself and his companions, in the window nearest to the door. He was probably aware of our approach, and had assumed an air of courageous indifference; his face was purposely averted towards the window, and he stirred not an inch while we were present. The other two men were at the upper end of the room. One of them, who was imperfectly seen in the dim light, had his back towards us, and was stooping over the fire, with his right arm on the mantel-piece, and his head sunk upon it. The other was leaning on the sill of the farthest window. The light fell full upon him, and communicated to his pale, haggard face, and disordered hair, an appearance which, at that distance, was ghastly. His cheek rested upon his hand; and, with his face a little raised, and his eyes wildly staring before him, he seemed to be unconsciously intent on counting the chinks in the opposite wall. We passed this room again afterwards. The first man was pacing up and down the court with a firm military step – he had been a soldier in the foot-guards – and a cloth cap jauntily thrown on one side of his head. He bowed respectfully to our conductor, and the salute was returned. The other two still remained in the positions we have described, and were as motionless as statues.*

A few paces up the yard, and forming a continuation of the building, in which are the two rooms we have just quitted, lie the condemned cells. The entrance is by a narrow and obscure staircase leading to a dark passage, in which a charcoal stove casts a lurid tint over the objects in its immediate vicinity, and diffuses something like warmth around. From the left-hand side of this passage, the massive door of every cell on the storey opens; and from it alone can they be approached. There are three of these passages, and three of these ranges of cells, one above the other; but in size, furniture and appearance, they are all precisely alike. Prior to the recorder's report being made, all the prisoners under sentence of death are removed from the day-room at five o'clock in the afternoon,

* These two men were executed shortly afterwards. The other was detained during His Majesty's pleasure.

Newgate – Exercise Yard

and locked up in these cells, where they are allowed a candle until ten o'clock; and here they remain until seven next morning. When the warrant for a prisoner's execution arrives, he is removed to the cells and confined in one of them until he leaves it for the scaffold. He is at liberty to walk in the yard; but, both in his walks and in his cell, he is constantly attended by a turnkey who never leaves him on any pretence.

We entered the first cell. It was a stone dungeon, eight feet long by six wide, with a bench at the upper end, under which were a common rug, a bible, and prayer-book. An iron candlestick was fixed into the wall at the side; and a small high window in the back admitted as much air and light as could struggle in between a double row of heavy, crossed iron bars. It contained no other furniture of any description.

Conceive the situation of a man, spending his last night on earth in this cell. Buoyed up with some vague and undefined hope of reprieve, he knew not why – indulging in some wild and visionary idea of escaping, he knew not how – hour after hour of the three preceding days allowed him for preparation, has fled with a speed which no man living would deem possible, for none but this dying man can know. He has wearied his friends with entreaties, exhausted the attendants with importunities, neglected in his feverish restlessness the timely warnings of his spiritual consoler; and, now that the illusion is at last dispelled, now that eternity is before him and guilt behind, now that his fears of death amount almost to madness, and an overwhelming sense of his helpless, hopeless state rushes upon him, he is lost and stupefied, and has neither thoughts to turn to, nor power to call upon, the Almighty Being, from whom alone he can seek mercy and forgiveness, and before whom his repentance can alone avail.

Hours have glided by, and still he sits upon the same stone bench with folded arms, heedless alike of the fast decreasing time before him, and the urgent entreaties of the good man at his side. The feeble light is wasting gradually, and the deathlike stillness of the street without, broken only by the rumbling of some passing vehicle which echoes mournfully through the empty yards, warns him that the night is waning fast away. The deep bell of St. Paul's strikes – one! He heard it; it has roused him. Seven hours left! He paces the narrow limits of his cell with rapid strides, cold drops of terror starting on his forehead, and every muscle of his frame quivering with agony. Seven hours! He suffers himself to be led to his seat, mechanically takes the bible which is placed in his hand, and tries to read and listen. No: his thoughts will wander. The book is torn and soiled by use – and like the book he read his lessons in, at school, just forty years ago! He has never bestowed a thought upon it, perhaps, since he left it as a child: and yet the place, the time, the room – nay, the very boys he played with, crowd as vividly before him as if they were scenes of yesterday; and some forgotten phrase, some childish word, rings in his ears like the echo of one uttered but a minute since. The voice of the clergyman recalls him to himself. He is reading from the

A Pickpocket in Custody

sacred book its solemn promises of pardon for repentance, and its awful denunciation of obdurate men. He falls upon his knees and clasps his hands to pray. Hush! what sound was that? He starts upon his feet. It cannot be two yet. Hark! Two quarters have struck; – the third – the fourth. It is! Six hours left. Tell him not of repentance! Six hours' repentance for eight times six years of guilt and sin! He buries his face in his hands, and throws himself on the bench.

Worn with watching and excitement, he sleeps, and the same unsettled state of mind pursues him in his dreams. An insupportable load is taken from his breast; he is walking with his wife in a pleasant field, with the bright sky above them, and a fresh and boundless prospect on every side – how different from the stone walls of Newgate! She is looking – not as she did when he saw her for the last time in that dreadful place, but as she used when he loved her – long, long ago, before misery and ill-treatment had altered her looks, and vice had changed his nature, and she is leaning upon his arm, and looking up into his face with tenderness and affection – and he does *not* strike her now, nor rudely shake her from him. And oh! how glad he is to tell her all he had forgotten in that last hurried interview, and to fall on his knees before her and fervently beseech her pardon for all the unkindness and cruelty that wasted her form and broke her heart! The scene suddenly changes. He is on his trial again: there are the judge and jury, and prosecutors, and witnesses, just as they were before. How full the court is – what a sea of heads – with a gallows, too, and a scaffold – and how all those people stare at *him*! Verdict, "Guilty." No matter; he will escape.

The night is dark and cold, the gates have been left open, and in an instant he is in the street, flying from the scene of his imprisonment like the wind. The streets are cleared, the open fields are gained and the broad, wide country lies before him. Onward he dashes in the midst of darkness, over hedge and ditch, through mud and pool, bounding from spot to spot with a speed and lightness, astonishing even to himself. At length he pauses; he must be safe from pursuit now; he will stretch himself on that bank and sleep till sunrise.

A period of unconsciousness succeeds. He wakes, cold and wretched. The dull, gray light of morning is stealing into the cell, and falls upon the form of the attendant turnkey. Confused by his dreams, he starts from his uneasy bed in momentary uncertainty. It is but momentary. Every object in the narrow cell is too frightfully real to admit of doubt or mistake. He is the condemned felon again, guilty and despairing; and in two hours more will be dead.

Sketches by Boz, *Chapter 25*

Captain Murderer

Dickens recounts here, after a visit to Rochester ("Dullborough") where he lived for part of his childhood, a story "introduced by my nurse before I was six years old" and told "hundreds of times". The nature of the story and the vividness of Dickens's detailed remembrance of it may explain something of the comic-macabre threads in his writing.

THE FIRST diabolical character who intruded himself on my peaceful youth (as I called to mind that day at Dullborough), was a certain Captain Murderer. This wretch must have been an off-shoot of the Blue Beard family, but I had no suspicion of the consanguinity in those times. His warning name would seem to have awakened no general prejudice against him, for he was admitted into the best society and possessed immense wealth. Captain Murderer's mission was matrimony, and the gratification of a cannibal appetite with tender brides. On his marriage morning, he always caused both sides of the way to church to be planted with curious flowers; and when his bride said, "Dear Captain Murderer, I never saw flowers like these before: what are they called?" he answered, "They are called Garnish for house-lamb," and laughed at his ferocious practical joke in a horrid manner, disquieting the minds of the noble bridal company, with a very sharp show of teeth, then displayed for the first time.

He made love in a coach and six, and married in a coach and twelve, and all his horses were milk-white horses with one red spot on the back which he caused to be hidden by the harness. For, the spot *would* come there, though every horse was milk-white when Captain Murderer bought him. And the spot was young bride's blood. (To this terrific point I am indebted for my first personal experience of a shudder and cold beads on the forehead.)

When Captain Murderer had made an end of feasting and revelry, and had dismissed the noble guests, and was alone with his wife on the day month after their marriage, it was his whimsical custom to produce a golden rolling-pin and a silver pie-board. Now, there was this special feature in the Captain's courtships, that he always asked if the young lady could make pie-crust; and if she couldn't by nature or education, she was taught.

Well. When the bride saw Captain Murderer produce the golden rolling-pin and silver pie-board, she remembered this, and turned up her laced-silk sleeves to make a pie. The Captain brought out a silver pie-dish of immense capacity, and the Captain brought out flour and butter and eggs and all things needful, except the inside of the pie; of materials for the staple of the pie itself, the Captain brought out none. Then said the lovely bride, "Dear Captain Murderer, what pie is this to be?" He replied, "A meat pie." Then said the lovely bride, "Dear Captain Murderer, I see no meat."

The Captain humorously retorted, "Look in the glass." She looked in the glass, but still she saw no meat, and then the Captain roared with laughter, and suddenly frowning and drawing his sword, bade her roll out the crust. So she rolled out the crust, dropping large tears upon it all the time because he was so cross, and when she had lined the dish with crust and had cut the crust all ready to fit the top, the Captain called out, "*I* see the meat in the glass!" And the bride looked up at the glass, just in time to see the Captain cutting her head off; and he chopped her in pieces, and peppered her, and salted her, and put her in the pie, and sent it to the baker's, and ate it all, and picked the bones.

Captain Murderer went on in this way, prospering exceedingly, until he came to choose a bride from two twin sisters, and at first didn't know which to choose. For, though one was fair and the other dark, they were both equally beautiful. But the fair twin loved him, and the dark twin hated him, so he chose the fair one. The dark twin would have prevented the marriage if she could, but she couldn't; however, on the night before it, much suspecting Captain Murderer, she stole out and climbed his garden wall, and looked in at his window through a chink in the shutter, and saw him having his teeth filed sharp. Next day she listened all day, and heard him make his joke about the house-lamb. And that day month, he had the paste rolled out, and cut the fair twin's head off, and chopped her in pieces, and peppered her, and salted her, and put her in the pie, and sent it to the baker's, and ate it all, and picked the bones.

Now, the dark twin had had her suspicions much increased by the filing of the Captain's teeth, and again by the house-lamb joke. Putting all things together when he gave out that her sister was dead, she divined the truth, and determined to be revenged. So, she went up to Captain Murderer's house, and knocked at the knocker and pulled at the bell, and when the Captain came to the door, said: "Dear Captain Murderer, marry me next, for I always loved you and was jealous of my sister." The Captain took it as a compliment, and made a polite answer, and the marriage was quickly arranged. On the night before it, the bride again climbed to his window, and again saw him having his teeth filed sharp. At this sight she laughed such a terrible laugh at the chink in the shutter, that the Captain's blood curdled, and he said: "I hope nothing has disagreed with me!" At that, she laughed again, a still more terrible laugh, and the shutter was opened and search made, but she was nimbly gone, and there was no one. Next day they went to church in a coach and twelve, and were married. And that day month, she rolled the pie-crust out, and Captain Murderer cut her head off, and chopped her in pieces, and peppered her, and salted her, and put her in the pie, and sent it to the baker's, and ate it all, and picked the bones.

But before she began to roll out the paste she had taken a deadly poison of a most awful character, distilled from toads' eyes and spiders' knees; and Captain Murderer had hardly picked her last bone, when he began to swell, and to turn blue, and to be all over spots, and to scream. And he went on swelling and turning bluer, and being more all over spots and screaming, until he reached from floor to ceiling and from wall to wall; and then, at one o'clock in the morning, he blew up with a loud explosion. At the sound of it, all the milk-white horses in the stables broke their halters and went mad, and then they galloped over everybody in Captain Murderer's house (beginning with the family blacksmith who had filed his teeth) until the whole were dead, and then they galloped away.

The Uncommercial Traveller, *Chapter 15*

Death of a lawyer

Lady Dedlock has a guilty secret and Mr. Tulkinghorn, lawyer to the aristocracy, has found it out and is now prepared to tell the husband, Sir Leicester Dedlock, that his wife has had an illegitimate daughter. This is Esther Summerson, the heroine and co-narrator of **Bleak House**. *This novel is written very much as a mystery story and a murder is about to take place. One of the mysteries is Tulkinghorn himself, a keeper of secrets and a relentless discoverer of them. He is a very powerful and disturbing figure in the book whose motivation is hidden from us. He has a sense of duty that is implacable and would be malevolent here if he had any feelings. He appears not to, apart from respect for Lady Dedlock as a worthy adversary.*

For a little while they are silent. Lady Dedlock has eaten no dinner, but has twice or thrice poured out water with a steady hand and drunk it. She rises from table, takes a lounging-chair, and reclines in it, shading her face. There is nothing in her manner to express weakness or excite compassion. It is thoughtful, gloomy, concentrated. "This woman," thinks Mr. Tulkinghorn, standing on the hearth, again a dark object closing up her view, "is a study."

He studies her at his leisure, not speaking for a time. She too studies something at her leisure. She is not the first to speak, appearing indeed so unlikely to be so, though he stood there until midnight, that even he is driven upon breaking silence.

"Lady Dedlock, the most disagreeable part of this business interview remains, but it is business. Our agreement is broken. A lady of your sense and strength of character will be prepared for my now declaring it void and taking my own course."

"I am quite prepared."

Mr. Tulkinghorn inclines his head. "That is all I have to trouble you with, Lady Dedlock."

She stops him as he is moving out of the room by asking, "This is the notice I was to receive? I wish not to misapprehend you."

"Not exactly the notice you were to receive, Lady Dedlock, because the contemplated notice supposed the agreement to have been observed. But virtually the same, virtually the same. The difference is merely in a lawyer's mind."

"You intend to give me no other notice?"

"You are right. No."

"Do you contemplate undeceiving Sir Leicester tonight?"

"A home question!" says Mr. Tulkinghorn with a slight smile and cautiously shaking his head at the shaded face. "No, not tonight."

"Tomorrow?"

"All things considered, I had better decline answering that question, Lady Dedlock. If I were to say I don't know when, exactly, you would not believe me, and it would answer no purpose. It may be tomorrow. I would rather say no more. You are prepared, and I hold out no expectations which circumstances might fail to justify. I wish you good evening."

She removes her hand, turns her pale face towards him as he walks silently to the door, and stops him once again as he is about to open it.

"Do you intend to remain in the house any time? I heard you were writing in the library. Are you going to return there?"

"Only for my hat. I am going home."

She bows her eyes rather than her head, the movement is so slight and curious, and he withdraws. Clear of the room he looks at his watch but is inclined to doubt it by a minute or thereabouts. There is a splendid clock upon the staircase, famous, as splendid clocks not often are, for its accuracy. "And what do *you* say," Mr. Tulkinghorn inquires, referring to it. "What do you say?"

If it said now, "Don't go home!" What a famous clock, hereafter, if it said tonight of all the nights that it has counted off, to this old man of all the young and old men who have ever stood before it, "Don't go home!" With its sharp clear bell it strikes three quarters after seven and ticks on again. "Why, you are worse than I thought you," says Mr. Tulkinghorn, muttering reproof to his watch. "Two minutes wrong? At this rate you won't last my time." What a watch to return good for evil if it ticked in answer, "Don't go home!"

He passes out into the streets and walks on, with his hands behind him, under the shadow of the lofty houses, many of whose mysteries, difficulties, mortgages, delicate affairs of all kinds, are treasured up within his old black satin waistcoat. He is in the confidence of the very bricks and mortar. The high chimney-stacks telegraph family secrets to him. Yet there is not a voice in a mile of them to whisper, "Don't go home!"

Through the stir and motion of the commoner streets; through the roar and jar of many vehicles, many feet, many voices; with the blazing shop-lights lighting him on, the west wind blowing him on, and the crowd pressing him on, he is pitilessly urged upon his way, and nothing meets him murmuring, "Don't go home!" Arrived at last in his dull room to light his candles, and look round and up, and see the Roman* pointing from the ceiling, there is no new significance in the Roman's hand tonight or in the flutter of the attendant groups to give him the late warning, "Don't come here!"

It is a moonlight night, but the moon, being past the full, is only now rising over the great wilderness of London. The stars are shining as they shone above the turret-leads at Chesney Wold. This woman, as he has of late been so accustomed to call her, looks out upon them. Her soul is turbulent within her; she is sick at heart and restless. The large rooms are too cramped and close. She cannot endure their restraint and will walk alone in a neighbouring garden.

Too capricious and imperious in all she does to be the cause of much surprise in those about her as to anything she does, this woman, loosely muffled, goes out into the moonlight. Mercury* attends with the key. Having opened the garden-gate, he delivers the key into his Lady's hands at her request and is bidden to go back. She will walk there some time to ease her aching head. She may be an hour, she may be more. She needs no further escort. The gate shuts upon its spring with a clash, and he leaves her passing on into the dark shade of some trees.

A fine night, and a bright large moon, and multitudes of stars. Mr. Tulkinghorn, in repairing to his cellar and in opening and shutting those resounding doors, has to cross a little prison-like yard. He looks up casually, thinking what a fine night, what a bright large moon, what multitudes of stars! A quiet night, too.

A very quiet night. When the moon shines very brilliantly, a solitude and stillness seem to proceed from her that influence even crowded places full of life. Not only is it a still night on dusty high roads and on hill-summits, whence a wide expanse of country may be seen in repose, quieter and quieter as it spreads away into a fringe of trees against the sky with the grey ghost of a bloom upon them; not only is it a still night in gardens and in woods, and on the river where the water-meadows are fresh and green, and the stream sparkles on among pleasant islands, murmuring weirs, and whispering rushes; not only does the stillness attend it as it flows where houses cluster thick, where many bridges are reflected in it, where wharves and shipping make it black and awful, where it winds from these disfigurements through marshes whose grim beacons stand like skeletons washed ashore, where it expands through the bolder region of rising grounds, rich in cornfield wind-mill and steeple, and where it mingles with the ever-heaving sea; not only is it a

* the Roman: a figure painted on the ceiling of Tulkinghorn's room and a recurring reference in Dickens's descriptions of the chambers in Lincoln's Inn Fields.

* Mercury: a frequent ironic reference in the book to any one of the powdered and bewigged footmen in attendance on aristocrats such as Lady Dedlock.

still night on the deep, and on the shore where the watcher stands to see the ship with her spread wings cross the path of light that appears to be presented to only him; but even on this stranger's wilderness of London there is some rest. Its steeples and towers and its one great dome grow more ethereal; its smoky house-tops lose their grossness in the pale effulgence; the noises that arise from the streets are fewer and are softened, and the footsteps on the pavements pass more tranquilly away. In these fields of Mr. Tulkinghorn's inhabiting, where the shepherds play on Chancery pipes that have no stop, and keep their sheep in the fold by hook and by crook until they have shorn them exceeding close, every noise is merged, this moonlight night, into a distant ringing hum, as if the city were a vast glass, vibrating.

What's that? Who fired a gun or pistol? Where was it?

The few foot-passengers start, stop, and stare about them. Some windows and doors are opened, and people come out to look. It was a loud report and echoed and rattled heavily. It shook one house, or so a man says who was passing. It has aroused all the dogs in the neighbourhood, who bark vehemently. Terrified cats scamper across the road. While the dogs are yet barking and howling – there is one dog howling like a demon – the church-clocks, as if they were startled too, begin to strike. The hum from the streets, likewise, seems to swell into a shout. But it is soon over. Before the last clock begins to strike ten, there is a lull. When it has ceased, the fine night, the bright large moon, and multitudes of stars, are left at peace again.

Has Mr. Tulkinghorn been disturbed? His windows are dark and quiet, and his door is shut. It must be something unusual indeed to bring him out of his shell. Nothing is heard of him, nothing is seen of him. What power of cannon might it take to shake that rusty old man out of his immovable composure?

For many years the persistent Roman has been pointing, with no particular meaning, from that ceiling. It is not likely that he has any new meaning in him tonight. Once pointing, always pointing – like any Roman, or even Briton, with a single idea. There he is, no doubt, in his impossible attitude, pointing, unavailingly, all night long. Moonlight, darkness, dawn, sunrise, day. There he is still, eagerly pointing, and no one minds him.

But a little after the coming of the day come people to clean the rooms. And either the Roman has some new meaning in him, not expressed before, or the foremost of them goes wild, for looking up at his outstretched hand and looking down at what is below it, that person shrieks and flies. The others, looking in as the first one looked, shriek and fly too, and there is an alarm in the street.

What does it mean? No light is admitted into the darkened chamber, and people unaccustomed to it enter, and treading softly but heavily, carry a weight into the bedroom and lay it down. There is whispering and wondering all day, strict search of every corner, careful tracing of steps, and careful noting of the disposition of every article of furniture. All eyes look up at the Roman, and all voices murmur, "If he could only tell what he saw!"

He is pointing at a table with a bottle (nearly full of wine) and a glass upon it and two candles that were blown out suddenly soon after being lighted. He is pointing at an empty chair and at a stain upon the ground before it that might be almost covered with a hand. These objects lie directly within his range. An excited imagination might suppose that there was something in them so terrific as to drive the rest of the composition, not only the attendant big-legged boys, but the clouds and flowers and pillars too – in short, the very body and soul of Allegory, and all the brains it has – stark mad. It happens surely that every one who comes into the darkened room and looks at these things looks up at the Roman and that he is invested in all eyes with mystery and awe, as if he were a paralysed dumb witness.

So it shall happen surely, through many years to come, that ghostly stories shall be told of the stain upon the floor, so easy to be covered, so hard to be got out, and that the Roman, pointing from the ceiling shall point, so long as dust and damp and spiders spare him, with far greater significance than he ever had in Mr. Tulkinghorn's time, and with a deadly meaning. For Mr. Tulkinghorn's time is over for evermore, and the Roman pointed at the murderous hand uplifted against his life, and pointed helplessly at him, from night to morning, lying face downward on the floor, shot through the heart.

Bleak House, *Chapter 48*

A public execution

Dickens attended three, possibly four public executions. **Pictures from Italy** *was written after a year spent touring that country in 1844–45 and it includes this description of a public beheading in Rome. The mixture of fascination and disgust in the graphic account is not untypical of Dickens's writing on such matters.*

On one Saturday morning (the eighth of March), a man was beheaded here. Nine or ten months before, he had waylaid a Bavarian countess, travelling as a pilgrim to Rome – alone and on foot, of course – and performing, it is said, that act of piety for the fourth time. He saw her change a piece of gold at Viterbo, where he lived; followed her; bore her company on her journey for some forty miles or more, on the treacherous pretext of protecting her; attacked her, in the fulfilment of his unrelenting purpose, on the Campagna, within a very short distance of Rome, near to what is called (but what is not) the Tomb of Nero; robbed her; and beat her to death with her own pilgrim's staff. He was newly married, and gave some of her apparel to his wife; saying that he had bought it at a fair. She, however, who had seen the pilgrim-countess passing through their town, recognised some trifle as having belonged to her. Her husband then told her what he had done. She, in confession, told a priest; and the man was taken, within four days after the commission of the murder.

There are no fixed times for the administration of justice, or its execution, in this unaccountable country; and he had been in prison ever since. On the Friday, as he was dining with the other prisoners, they came and told him he was to be beheaded next morning, and took him away. It is very unusual to execute in Lent; but his crime being a very bad one, it was deemed advisable to make an example of him at that time, when great numbers of pilgrims were coming towards Rome, from all parts, for the Holy Week. I heard of this on the Friday evening, and saw the bills up at the churches, calling on the people to pray for the criminal's soul. So, I determined to go, and see him executed.

The beheading was appointed for fourteen and a-half o'clock, Roman time: or a quarter before nine in the forenoon. I had two friends with me, and as we did not know but that the crowd might be very great, we were on the spot by half-past seven. The place of execution was near the church of San Giovanni decolláto (a doubtful compliment to Saint John the Baptist) in one of the impassable back streets without any footway, of which a great part of Rome is composed – a street of rotten houses, which do not seem to belong to anybody, and do not seem to have ever been inhabited, and certainly were never built on any plan, or for any particular purpose, and have no window-sashes, and are a little like deserted breweries, and might be warehouses but for having nothing in them. Opposite to one of these, a white house, the scaffold was built. An untidy, unpainted, uncouth, crazy-looking thing of course: some seven feet high, perhaps: with a tall, gallows-shaped frame rising above it, in which was the knife, charged with a ponderous mass of iron, all ready to descend, and glittering brightly in the morning sun, whenever it looked out, now and then, from behind a cloud.

There were not many people lingering about; and these were kept at a considerable distance from the scaffold, by parties of the Pope's dragoons. Two or three hundred foot-soldiers were under arms, standing at ease in clusters here and there; and the officers were walking up and down in twos and threes, chatting together, and smoking cigars.

At the end of the street, was an open space, where there would be a dust-heap, and piles of broken crockery, and mounds of vegetable refuse, but for such things being thrown anywhere and everywhere in Rome, and favouring no particular sort of locality. We got into a kind of wash-house, belonging to a dwelling-house on this spot; and standing there in an old cart, and on a heap of cart-wheels piled against the wall, looking, through a large grated window, at the scaffold, and straight down the street beyond it, until, in consequence of its turning off abruptly to the left, our perspective was brought to a sudden termination, and had a corpulent officer, in a cocked hat, for its crowning feature.

Nine o'clock struck, and ten o'clock struck, and nothing happened. All the bells of all the churches rang as usual. A little parliament of dogs assembled in the open space, and chased each other, in and out among the soldiers. Fierce-looking Romans of the lowest class, in blue cloaks, russet cloaks, and rags uncloaked, came and went, and talked together. Women and children fluttered, on the skirts of the scanty crowd. One large muddy spot was left quite bare, like a bald place on a man's head. A cigar-merchant, with an earthen pot of charcoal ashes in one hand, went up and down, crying his wares. A pastry-merchant divided his attention between the scaffold and his customers. Boys tried to climb up walls, and tumbled down again. Priests and monks elbowed a passage for themselves among the people, and stood on tiptoe for a sight of the knife: then went away. Artists, in inconceivable hats of the middle-ages, and beards (thank Heaven!) of no age at all, flashed picturesque scowls about them from their stations in the throng. One gentleman (connected with the fine arts, I presume) went up and down in a pair of Hessian-boots, with a red beard hanging down on his breast, and his long and bright red hair, plaited into two tails, one on either side of his head, which fell over his shoulders in front of him, very nearly to his waist, and were carefully entwined and braided!

Eleven o'clock struck; and still nothing happened. A rumour got about, among the crowd, that the criminal would not confess; in which case, the priests would keep him until the Ave Maria (sunset); for it is their merciful custom never finally to turn the crucifix away from a man at that pass, as one refusing to be shriven, and consequently a sinner abandoned of the Saviour, until then. People began to drop off. The officers shrugged their shoulders and looked doubtful. The dragoons, who came riding up below our window, every now and then, to order an unlucky hackney-coach or cart away, as soon as it had comfortably established itself, and was covered with exulting people (but never before), became imperious, and quick-tempered. The bald place hadn't a straggling hair upon it; and the corpulent officer, crowning the perspective, took a world of snuff.

Suddenly, there was a noise of trumpets. "Attention!" was among the foot-soldiers instantly. They were marched up to the scaffold and formed round it. The dragoons galloped to their near stations too. The guillotine became the centre of a wood of bristling bayonets and shining sabres. The people closed round nearer, on the flank of the soldiery. A long straggling stream of men and boys, who had accompanied the procession from the prison, came pouring into the open space. The bald spot was scarcely distinguishable from the rest. The cigar and pastry-merchants resigned all thoughts of business, for the moment, and abandoning themselves wholly to pleasure, got good situations in the crowd. The perspective ended, now, in a troop of dragoons. And the corpulent officer, sword in hand, looked hard at a church close to him, which he could see, but we, the crowd, could not.

After a short delay, some monks were seen approaching to the scaffold from this church; and above their heads, coming on slowly and gloomily, the effigy of Christ upon the cross, canopied with black. This was carried round the foot of the scaffold, to the front, and turned towards the criminal, that he might see it to the last. It was hardly in its place, when he appeared on the platform, bare-footed; his hands bound; and with the collar and neck of his shirt cut away, almost to the shoulder. A young man – six-and-twenty – vigorously made, and well-shaped. Face pale; small dark moustache; and dark brown hair.

He had refused to confess, it seemed, without first having his wife brought to see him; and they had sent an escort for her, which had occasioned the delay.

He immediately kneeled down, below the knife. His neck fitting into a hole, made for the purpose, in a cross plank, was shut down, by another plank above; exactly like the pillory. Immediately below him was a leathern bag. And into it his head rolled instantly.

The executioner was holding it by the hair, and walking with it round the scaffold, showing it to the people, before one quite knew that the knife had fallen heavily, and with a rattling sound.

When it had travelled round the four sides of the scaffold, it was set upon a pole in front – a little patch of black and white, for the long street to stare at, and the flies to settle on. The eyes were turned upward, as if he had avoided the sight of the leathern bag, and looked to the crucifix. Every tinge and hue of life had left it in that instant. It was dull, cold, livid, wax. The body also.

There was a great deal of blood. When we left the window, and went close up to the scaffold, it was very dirty; one of the two men who were throwing water over it, turning to help the other lift the body into a shell, picked his way as through mire. A strange appearance was the apparent annihilation of the neck. The head was taken off so close, that it seemed as if the knife had narrowly escaped crushing the jaw, or shaving off the ear; and the body looked as if there were nothing left above the shoulder.

Nobody cared, or was at all affected. There was no manifestation of disgust, or pity, or indignation, or sorrow. My empty pockets were tried, several times, in the crowd immediately below the scaffold, as the corpse was being put into its coffin. It was an ugly, filthy, careless, sickening spectacle; meaning nothing but butchery beyond the momentary interest, to the one wretched actor. Yes! Such a sight has one meaning and one warning. Let me not forget it. The speculators in the lottery, station themselves at favourable points for counting the gouts of blood that spirt out, here or there; and buy that number. It is pretty sure to have a run upon it.

The body was carted away in due time, the knife cleansed, the scaffold taken down, and all the hideous apparatus removed. The executioner: an outlaw *ex officio** (what a satire on the Punishment!) who dare not, for his life, cross the Bridge of St. Angelo but to do his work: retreated to his lair, and the show was over.

Pictures from Italy, "*Rome*"

* *ex officio*: by virtue of his office (as executioner), he was shunned by the townsfolk.

Pip in peril

Orlick, who has lured the grown-up Pip to the disused limekilns near Joe Gargery's forge, where they both used to work, has had a deep resentment of Pip since Pip's early years. Orlick reveals here that he struck the blow that brain-damaged Pip's older sister, Mrs. Joe, who brought Pip up. This is one of Dickens's studies of motiveless malignity and Pip is in very grave danger.

"Now," said a suppressed voice with an oath, "I've got you!"

"What is this?" I cried, struggling. "Who is it? Help, help, help!"

Not only were my arms pulled close to my sides, but the pressure on my bad arm caused me exquisite pain. Sometimes, a strong man's hand, sometimes a strong man's breast, was set against my mouth to deaden my cries, and with a hot breath always close to me, I struggled ineffectually in the dark, while I was fastened tight to the wall. "And now," said the suppressed voice with another oath, "call out again, and I'll make short work of you!"

Faint and sick with the pain of my injured arm, bewildered by the surprise, and yet conscious how easily this threat could be put in execution, I desisted, and tried to ease my arm were it ever so little. But, it was bound too tight for that. I felt as if, having been burnt before, it were now being boiled.

The sudden exclusion of the night and the substitution of black darkness in its place, warned me that the man had closed a shutter. After groping about for a little, he found the flint and steel he wanted, and began to strike a light. I strained my sight upon the sparks that fell among the tinder, and upon which he breathed and breathed, match in hand, but I could only see his lips, and the blue point of the match; even those, but fitfully. The tinder was damp – no wonder there – and one after another the sparks died out.

The man was in no hurry, and struck again with the flint and steel. As the sparks fell thick and bright about him, I could see his hands, and touches of his face, and could make out that he was seated and bending over the table; but nothing more. Presently I saw his blue lips again, breathing on the tinder, and then a flare of light flashed up, and showed me Orlick.

Whom I had looked for, I don't know. I had not looked for him. Seeing him, I felt that I was in a dangerous strait indeed, and I kept my eyes upon him.

He lighted the candle from the flaring match with great deliberation, and dropped the match, and trod it out. Then, he put the candle away from him on the table, so that he could see me, and sat with his arms folded on the table and looked at me. I made out that I was fastened to a stout perpendicular ladder a few inches from the wall – a fixture there – the means of ascent to the loft above.

"Now," said he, when we had surveyed one another for some time, "I've got you."

"Unbind me. Let me go!"

"Ah!" he returned, "*I'll* let you go. I'll let you go to the moon, I'll let you go to the stars. All in good time."

"Why have you lured me here?"

"Don't you know?" said he, with a deadly look.

"Why have you set upon me in the dark?"

"Because I mean to do it all myself. One keeps a secret better than two. Oh you enemy, you enemy!"

His enjoyment of the spectacle I furnished, as he sat with his arms folded on the table, shaking his head at me and hugging himself, had a malignity in it that made me tremble. As I watched him in silence, he put his hand into the corner at his side, and took up a gun with a brass-bound stock.

"Do you know this?" said he, making as if he would take aim at me. "Do you know where you saw it afore? Speak, wolf!"

"Yes," I answered.

"You cost me that place. You did. Speak!"

"What else could I do?"

"You did that, and that would be enough, without more. How dared you to come betwixt me and a young woman I liked?"

"When did I?"

"When didn't you? It was you as always give Old Orlick a bad name to her."

"You gave it to yourself; you gained it for yourself. I could have done you no harm, if you had done yourself none."

"You're a liar. And you'll take any pains, and spend any money, to drive me out of this country, will you?" said he, repeating my words to Biddy* in the last interview I had with her. "Now, I'll tell you a piece of information. It was never so well worth your while to get me out of this country as it is tonight. Ah! If it was all your money twenty times told, to the last brass farden!" As he shook his heavy hand at me, with his mouth snarling like a tiger's, I felt that it was true.

"What are you going to do to me?"

"I'm a going," said he, bringing his fist down upon the table with a

* Biddy: the orphan girl who teaches Pip to read when she comes as a housekeeper after Orlick's savage attack on Mrs. Joe.

heavy blow, and rising as the blow fell, to give it greater force, "I'm a going to have your life!"

He leaned forward staring at me, slowly unclenched his hand and drew it across his mouth as if his mouth watered for me, and sat down again.

"You was always in Old Orlick's way since ever you was a child. You goes out of his way, this present night. He'll have no more on you. You're dead."

I felt that I had come to the brink of my grave. For a moment I looked wildly round my trap for any chance of escape; but there was none.

"More than that," said he, folding his arms on the table again, "I won't have a rag of you, I won't have a bone of you, left on earth. I'll put your body in the kiln – I'd carry two such to it, on my shoulders – and, let people suppose what they may of you, they shall never know nothing."

My mind, with inconceivable rapidity, followed out all the consequences of such a death. Estella's father would believe I had deserted him, would be taken, would die accusing me; even Herbert would doubt me, when he compared the letter I had left for him, with the fact that I had called at Miss Havisham's gate for only a moment; Joe and Biddy would never know how sorry I had been that night; none would ever know what I had suffered, how true I had meant to be, what an agony I had passed through. The death close before me was terrible, but far more terrible than death was the dread of being misremembered after death. And so quick were my thoughts, that I saw myself despised by unborn generations – Estella's children, and their children – while the wretch's words were yet on his lips.

"Now, wolf," said he, "afore I kill you like any other beast – which is wot I mean to do and wot I have tied you up for – I'll have a good look at you and a good goad at you. Oh, you enemy!"

It had passed through my thoughts to cry out for help again; though few could know better than I, the solitary nature of the spot, and the hopelessness of aid. But as he sat gloating over me, I was supported by a scornful detestation of him that sealed my lips. Above all things, I resolved that I would not entreat him, and that I would die making some last poor resistance to him. Softened as my thoughts of all the rest of men were in that dire extremity; humbly beseeching pardon, as I did, of Heaven; melted at heart, as I was, by the thought that I had taken no farewell, and never never now could take farewell, of those who were dear to me, or could explain myself to them, or ask for their compassion on my miserable errors; still, if I could have killed him, even in dying, I would have done it.

He had been drinking, and his eyes were red and bloodshot. Around his neck was slung a tin bottle, as I had often seen his meat and drink slung about him in other days. He brought the bottle to his lips, and took a fiery drink from it; and I smelt the strong spirits that I saw flash into his face.

"Wolf!" said he, folding his arms again, "Old Orlick's a going to tell you somethink. It was you as did for your shrew sister."

Again my mind, with its former inconceivable rapidity, had exhausted the whole subject of the attack upon my sister, her illness, and her death, before his slow and hesitating speech had formed these words.

"It was you, villain," said I.

"I tell you it was your doing – I tell you it was done through you," he retorted, catching up the gun, and making a blow with the stock at the vacant air between us. "I come upon her from behind, as I come upon you tonight. *I* giv' it her! I left her for dead, and if there had been a limekiln as nigh her as there is now nigh you, she shouldn't have come to life again. But it warn't Old Orlick as did it; it was you. You was favoured, and he was bullied and beat. Old Orlick bullied and beat, eh? Now you pays for it. You done it; now you pays for it."

He drank again, and became more ferocious. I saw by his tilting of the bottle that there was no great quantity left in it. I distinctly understood that he was working himself up with its contents, to make an end of me. I knew that every drop it held, was a drop of my life. I knew that when I was changed into a part of the vapour that had crept towards me but a little while before, like my own warning ghost, he would do as he had done in my sister's case – make all haste to the town, and be seen slouching about there, drinking at the ale-houses. My rapid mind pursued him to the town, made a picture of the street with him in it, and contrasted its lights and life with the lonely marsh and the white vapour creeping over it, into which I should have dissolved.

It was not only that I could have summed up years and years and years while he said a dozen words, but that what he did say presented pictures to me, and not mere words. In the excited and exalted state of my brain, I could not think of a place without seeing it, or of persons without seeing them. It is impossible to over-state the vividness of these images, and yet I was so intent, all the time, upon him himself – who would not be intent on the tiger crouching to spring! – that I knew of the slightest action of his fingers. . . . .

Of a sudden, he stopped, took the cork out of his bottle, and tossed it away. Light as it was, I heard it fall like a plummet. He swallowed slowly, tilting up the bottle by little and little, and now he looked at me no more. The last few drops of liquor he poured into the palm of his hand, and licked up. Then, with a sudden hurry of violence and swearing horribly, he threw the bottle from him, and stooped; and I saw in his hand a stone-hammer with a long heavy handle.

Great Expectations, *Chapter 53*

The Storming of Newgate

Barnaby Rudge was Dickens's fifth novel and his first historical one. It is set in the eighteenth century at the time of the Gordon riots of 1780 which were caused by religious strife between Protestants and Catholics. A London mob is storming Newgate Prison to set the prisoners free. Barnaby Rudge, a simpleton, is caught up in the rioting and is used as a dupe by its leaders.

NOW, NOW, the door was down. Now they came rushing through the jail, calling to each other in the vaulted passages; clashing the iron gates dividing yard from yard; beating at the doors of cells and wards; wrenching off bolts and locks and bars; tearing down the door-posts to get men out; endeavouring to drag them by main force through gaps and windows where a child could scarcely pass; whooping and yelling without a moment's rest; and running through the heat and flames as if they were cased in metal. By their legs, their arms, the hair upon their heads, they dragged the prisoners out. Some threw themselves upon their captives as they got towards the door, and tried to file away their irons; some danced about them with a frenzied joy, and rent their clothes, and were ready, as it seemed, to tear them limb from limb. Now a party of a dozen men came darting through the yard into which the murderer cast fearful glances from his darkened window; dragging a prisoner along the ground whose dress they had nearly torn from his body in their mad eagerness to set him free, and who was bleeding and senseless in their hands. Now a score of prisoners ran to and fro, who had lost themselves in the intricacies of the prison, and were so bewildered with the noise and glare that they knew not where to turn or what to do, and still cried out for help, as loudly as before.

Anon some famished wretch whose theft had been a loaf of bread, or scrap of butcher's meat, came skulking past, barefooted – going slowly away because that jail, his house, was burning; not because he had any other, or had friends to meet, or old haunts to revisit, or any liberty to gain but liberty to starve and die. And then a knot of highwaymen went trooping by, conducted by the friends they had among the crowd, who muffled their fetters as they went along, with handkerchiefs and bands of hay, and wrapped them in coats and cloaks, and gave them drink from bottles, and held it to their lips, because of their handcuffs which there was no time to remove. All this, and Heaven knows how much more, was done amidst a noise, a hurry, and distraction, like nothing that we know of, even in our dreams; which seemed for ever on the rise, and never to decrease for the space of a single instant.

He* was still looking down from his window upon these things, when a band of men with torches, ladders, axes, and many kinds of weapons, poured into the yard, and hammering at his door, inquired if there were any prisoner within. He left the window when he saw them coming, and drew back into the remotest corner of the cell; but although he returned them no answer, they had a fancy that some one was inside, for they presently set ladders against it, and began to tear away the bars at the casement; not only that, indeed, but with pickaxes to hew down the very stones in the wall.

As soon as they had made a breach at the window, large enough for the admission of a man's head, one of them thrust in a torch and looked all round the room. He followed this man's gaze until it rested on himself, and heard him demand why he had not answered, but made him no reply.

In the general surprise and wonder, they were used to this; without saying anything more, they enlarged the breach until it was large enough to admit the body of a man, and then came dropping down upon the floor, one after another, until the cell was full. They caught him up among them, handed him to the window, and those who stood upon the ladders passed him down upon the pavement of the yard. Then the rest came out, one after another, and, bidding him fly, and lose no time, or the way would be choked up, hurried away to rescue others.

It seemed not a minute's work from first to last. He staggered to his feet, incredulous of what had happened, when the yard was filled again, and a crowd rushed on, hurrying Barnaby among them. In another minute – not so much: another minute! the same instant, with no lapse or interval between! – he and his son were being passed from hand to hand, through the dense crowd in the street, and were glancing backward at a burning pile which some one said was Newgate.

From the moment of their first entrance into the prison, the crowd dispersed themselves about it, and swarmed into every chink and crevice, as if they had a perfect acquaintance with its innermost parts, and bore in their minds an exact plan of the whole. For this immediate knowledge of the place, they were, no doubt, in a great degree, indebted to the hangman,* who stood in the lobby, directing some to go this way, some that, and some the other; and who materially assisted in bringing

* Barnaby Rudge's father, imprisoned for murder – Barnaby is with him in his cell.

* the hangman: based on the real Ned Dennis who joined in the rioting. Dickens's character takes a pride in his job!

about the wonderful rapidity with which the release of the prisoners was effected.

But this functionary of the law reserved one important piece of intelligence, and kept it snugly to himself. When he had issued his instructions relative to every other part of the building, and the mob were dispersed from end to end, and busy at their work, he took a bundle of keys from a kind of cupboard in the wall, and going by a kind of passage near the chapel (it joined the governor's house, and was then on fire), betook himself to the condemned cells, which were a series of small, strong, dismal rooms, opening on a low gallery, guarded, at the end at which he entered, by a strong iron wicket, and at its opposite extremity by two doors and a thick gate. Having double locked the wicket, and assured himself that the other entrances were well secured, he sat down on a bench in the gallery, and sucked the head of his stick with the utmost complacency, tranquility, and contentment.

It would have been strange enough, a man's enjoying himself in this quiet manner, while the prison was burning, and such a tumult was cleaving the air, though he had been outside the walls. But here, in the very heart of the building, and moreover with the prayers and cries of the four men under sentence sounding in his ears, and their hands, stretched out through the gratings in their cell-doors, clasped in frantic entreaty before his very eyes, it was particularly remarkable. Indeed, Mr. Dennis appeared to think it an uncommon circumstance, and to banter himself upon it; for he thrust his hat on one side as some men do when they are in a waggish humour, sucked the head of his stick with a higher relish, and smiled as though he would say, "Dennis, you're a rum dog; you're a queer fellow; you're capital company, Dennis, and quite a character!"

He sat in this way for some minutes, while the four men in the cells, certain that somebody had entered the gallery, but could not see who, gave vent to such piteous entreaties as wretches in their miserable condition may be supposed to have been inspired with: urging, whoever it was, to set them at liberty, for the love of Heaven; and protesting, with great fervour, and truly enough, perhaps, for the time, that if they escaped, they would amend their ways, and would never, never, never again do wrong before God or man, but would lead penitent and sober lives, and sorrowfully repent the crimes they had committed. The terrible energy with which they spoke, would have moved any person, no matter how good or just (if any good or just person could have strayed into that sad place that night), to have set them at liberty; and, while he would have left any other punishment to its free course, to have saved them from this last dreadful and repulsive penalty; which never turned a man inclined to evil, and has hardened thousands who were half inclined to good.

Mr. Dennis, who had been bred and matured in the good old school, and had administered the good old laws on the good old plan, always once and sometimes twice every six weeks, for a long time, bore these appeals with a deal of philosophy. Being at last, however, rather disturbed in his pleasant reflection by their repetition, he rapped at one of the doors with his stick, and cried:

"Hold your noise there, will you?"

At this they all cried together that they were to be hanged on the next day but one; and again implored his aid.

"Aid! For what!" said Mr. Dennis, playfully rapping the knuckles of the hand nearest him.

"To save us!" they cried.

"Oh, certainly," said Mr. Dennis, winking at the wall in the absence of any friend with whom he could humour the joke. "And so you're to be worked off, are you, brothers?"

"Unless we are released tonight," one of them cried, "we are dead men!"

"I tell you what it is," said the hangman, gravely; "I'm afraid, my friend, that you're not in that 'ere state of mind that's suitable to your condition, then; you're not a-going to be released: don't think it – Will you leave off that 'ere indecent row? I wonder you an't ashamed of yourselves, I do."

He followed up this reproof by rapping every set of knuckles one after the other, and having done so, resumed his seat again with a cheerful countenance.

"You've had law," he said, crossing his legs and elevating his eyebrows: "laws have been made a' purpose for you; a very handsome prison's been made a' purpose for you; a parson's kept a' purpose for you; a constitootional officer's appointed a' purpose for you; carts is maintained a' purpose for you – and yet you're not contented! – *Will* you hold that noise, you sir in the furthest?"

A groan was the only answer.

"So well as I can make out," said Mr. Dennis, in a tone of mingled badinage and remonstrance, "there's not a man among you. I begin to think I'm on the opposite side, and among the ladies; though for the matter of that, I've seen a many ladies face it out, in a manner that did honour to the sex. – You in number two, don't grind them teeth of yours. Worse manners," said the hangman, rapping at the door with his stick, "I never see in this place afore. I'm ashamed of you. You're a disgrace to the Bailey."

After pausing for a moment to hear if anything could be pleaded in justification, Mr. Dennis resumed in a sort of coaxing tone:

"Now look'ee here, you four. I'm come here to take care of you, and see that you an't burnt, instead of the other thing. It's no use your making any noise, for you won't be found out by them as has broken in, and you'll only be hoarse when you come to the speeches, – which is a pity. What I say in respect to the speeches always is, 'Give it mouth.' That's my maxim. Give it mouth. I've heerd," said the hangman, pulling off his hat to take his handkerchief from the crown and wipe his face, and then putting it on again a little more on one side than before, "I've heerd a eloquence on them boards – you know what boards I mean – and have heerd a degree of mouth given to them speeches, that they was as clear as a bell, and as good as a play. There's a pattern! And always, when a thing of this natur's to come off, what I stand up for, is, a proper frame of mind. Let's have a proper frame of mind, and we can go through with it, creditable – pleasant – sociable. Whatever you do (and I address myself, in particular, to you in the furthest), never snivel. I'd sooner by half, though I lose by it, see a man tear his clothes a' purpose to spile 'em before they come to me, than find him snivelling. It's ten to one a better frame of mind, every way!"

Barnaby Rudge, *Chapter 65*

Princess Puffer's den

Dickens's last novel, ***The Mystery of Edwin Drood,*** *contains a final mystery because Dickens died before he finished the story. Edwin Drood disappears in the novel and it seems likely he has been murdered. His uncle, John Jasper, the apparently respectable choirmaster of Cloisterham where the book is set, is a secret opium smoker. In London's Limehouse he visits for the second time the opium den of Princess Puffer and the conversation he has there may possibly provide psychological clues as to who the murderer really is.*

HE EATS without appetite, and soon goes forth again. Eastward and still eastward through the stale streets he takes his way, until he reaches his destination: a miserable court, specially miserable among many such.

He ascends a broken staircase, opens a door, looks into a dark stifling room, and says: "Are you alone here?"

"Alone, deary; worse luck for me, and better for you," replies a croaking voice. "Come in, come in, whoever you be: I can't see you till I light a match, yet I seem to know the sound of your speaking. I'm acquainted with you, ain't I?"

"Light your match, and try."

"So I will, deary, so I will; but my hand that shakes, as I can't lay it on a match all in a moment. And I cough so, that, put my matches where I may, I never find 'em there. They jump and start, as I cough and cough, like live things. Are you off a voyage, deary?"

"No."

"Not seafaring?"

"No."

"Well, there's land customers, and there's water customers. I'm a mother to both. Different from Jack Chinaman t'other side the court. He ain't a father to neither. It ain't in him. And he ain't got the true secret of mixing, though he charges as much as me that has, and more if he can get it. Here's a match, and now where's the candle? If my cough takes me, I shall cough out twenty matches afore I gets a light."

But she finds the candle, and lights it, before the cough comes on. It seizes her in the moment of success, and she sits down rocking herself to and fro, and gasping at intervals: "O, my lungs is awful bad! my lungs is wore away to cabbage-nets!" until the fit is over. During its continuance she has had no power of sight, or any other power not absorbed in the struggle; but as it leaves her, she begins to strain her eyes, and as soon as she is able to articulate, she cries, staring:

"Why, it's you!"

"Are you so surprised to see me?"

"I thought I never should have seen you again, deary. I thought you was dead, and gone to Heaven."

"Why?"

"I didn't suppose you could have kept away, alive, so long, from the poor old soul with the real receipt for mixing it. And you are in mourning too! Why didn't you come and have a pipe or two of comfort? Did they leave you money, perhaps, and so you didn't want comfort?"

"No."

"Who was they as died, deary?"

"A relative."

"Died of what, lovey?"

"Probably, Death."

"We are short tonight!" cries the woman, with a propitiatory laugh. "Short and snappish we are! But we're out of sorts for want of a smoke. We've got the all-overs, haven't us, deary? But this is the place to cure 'em in; this is the place where the all-overs is smoked off."

"You may make ready, then," replies the visitor, "as soon as you like."

He divests himself of his shoes, loosens his cravat, and lies across the foot of the squalid bed, with his head resting on his left hand.

"Now you begin to look like yourself," says the woman approvingly. "Now I begin to know my old customer indeed! Been trying to mix for yourself this long time, poppet?"

"I have been taking it now and then in my own way."

"Never take it your own way. It ain't good for trade, and it ain't good for you. Where's my ink-bottle, and where's my thimble, and where's my little spoon? He's going to take it in a artful form now, my deary dear!"

Entering on her process, and beginning to bubble and blow at the faint spark enclosed in the hollow of her hands, she speaks from time to time, in a tone of snuffling satisfaction, without leaving off. When he speaks, he does so without looking at her, and as if his thoughts were already roaming away by anticipation.

"I've got a pretty many smokes ready for you, first and last, haven't I, chuckey?"

"A good many."

"When you first come, you was quite new to it; warn't ye?"

"Yes, I was easily disposed of, then."

"But you got on in the world, and was able by and by to take your pipe with the best of 'em, warn't ye?"

"Ah; and the worst."

"It's just ready for you. What a sweet singer you was when you first come! Used to drop your head, and sing yourself off like a bird! It's ready for you now, deary."

He takes it from her with great care, and puts the mouthpiece to his lips. She seats herself beside him, ready to refill the pipe. After inhaling a few whiffs in silence, he doubtingly accosts her with:

"Is it as potent as it used to be?"

"What do you speak of, deary?"

"What should I speak of, but what I have in my mouth?"

"It's just the same. Always the identical same."

"It doesn't taste so. And it's slower."

"You've got more used to it, you see."

"That may be the cause, certainly. Look here." He stops, becomes dreamy, and seems to forget that he has invited her attention. She bends over him, and speaks in his ear.

"I'm attending to you. Says you just now, Look here. Says I now, I'm attending to ye. We was talking just before of your being used to it."

"I know all that. I was only thinking. Look here. Suppose you had something in your mind; something you were going to do."

"Yes, deary; something I was going to do?"

"But had not quite determined to do."

"Yes, deary."

"Might or might not do, you understand."

"Yes." With the point of a needle she stirs the contents of the bowl.

"Should you do it in your fancy, when you were lying here doing this?"

She nods her head. "Over and over again."

"Just like me! I did it over and over again. I have done it hundreds of thousands of times in this room."

"It's to be hoped it was pleasant to do, deary."

"It *was* pleasant to do!"

He says this with a savage air, and a spring or start at her. Quite unmoved she retouches and replenishes the contents of the bowl with her little spatula. Seeing her intent upon the occupation, he sinks into his former attitude.

"It was a journey, a difficult and dangerous journey. That was the subject in my mind. A hazardous and perilous journey, over abysses where a slip would be destruction. Look down, look down! You see what lies at the bottom there?"

Opium smoking – the Lascar's Room in Edwin Drood

He has darted forward to say it, and to point at the ground, as though at some imaginary object far beneath. The woman looks at him, as his spasmodic face approaches close to hers, and not at his pointing. She seems to know what the influence of her perfect quietude would be; if so, she has not miscalculated it, for he subsides again.

"Well; I have told you I did it here hundreds of thousands of times. What do I say? I did it millions and billions of times. I did it so often, and through such vast expanses of time, that when it was really done, it seemed not worth the doing, it was done so soon."

"That's the journey you have been away upon," she quietly remarks.

He glares at her as he smokes; and then, his eyes becoming filmy, answers: "That's the journey."

Silence ensues. His eyes are sometimes closed and sometimes open. The woman sits beside him, very attentive to the pipe, which is all the while at his lips.

"I'll warrant," she observes, when he has been looking fixedly at her for some consecutive moments, with a singular appearance in his eyes of seeming to see her a long way off, instead of so near him: "I'll warrant you made the journey in a many ways, when you made it so often?"

"No, always in one way."

"Always in the same way?"

"Ay."

"In the way in which it was really made at last?"

"Ay."

"And always took the same pleasure in harping on it?"

"Ay."

For the time he appears unequal to any other reply than this lazy monosyllabic assent. Probably to assure herself that it is not the assent of a mere automaton, she reverses the form of her next sentence.

"Did you never get tired of it, deary, and try to call up something else for a change?"

He struggles into a sitting posture, and retorts upon her: "What do you mean? What did I want? What did I come for?"

She gently lays him back again, and before returning him the instrument he has dropped, revives the fire in it with her own breath; then says to him, coaxingly:

"Sure, sure, sure! Yes, yes, yes! Now I go along with you. You was too quick for me. I see now. You come o' purpose to take the journey. Why, I might have known it, through its standing by you so."

He answers first with a laugh, and then with a passionate setting of his teeth: "Yes, I came on purpose. When I could not bear my life, I came to get the relief, and I got it. It WAS one! It WAS one!" This repetition with extraordinary vehemence, and the snarl of a wolf.

The Mystery of Edwin Drood, *Chapter 23*

Sikes and Nancy

*A famous episode from **Oliver Twist** in which Bill Sikes, the brutish lover of Nancy, kills her because she has tried to help Oliver and his connections, thus endangering Fagin's and Sikes's thieving activities. Dickens had enormous success with the Sikes and Nancy story at his public readings.*

"WOT NOW?" cried Sikes. "Wot do you look at a man so for?"

Fagin raised his right hand, and shook his trembling fore-finger in the air; but his passion was so great, that the power of speech was for the moment gone.

"Damme!" said Sikes, feeling in his breast with a look of alarm. "He's gone mad. I must look to myself here."

"No, no," rejoined Fagin, finding his voice. "It's not – you're not the person, Bill. I've no – no fault to find with you."

"Oh, you haven't, haven't you?" said Sikes, looking sternly at him, and ostentatiously passing a pistol into a more convenient pocket. "That's lucky – for one of us. Which one that is, don't matter."

"I've got that to tell you, Bill," said Fagin, drawing his chair nearer, "will make you worse than me."

"Aye?" returned the robber with an incredulous air. "Tell away! Look sharp, or Nance will think I'm lost."

"Lost!" cried Fagin. "She has pretty well settled that, in her own mind already."

Sikes looked with an aspect of great perplexity into the Jew's face, and reading no satisfactory explanation of the riddle there, clenched his coat collar in his huge hand and shook him soundly.

"Speak, will you!" he said; "or if you don't, it shall be for want of breath. Open your mouth and say wot you've got to say in plain words. Out with it, you thundering old cur, out with it!"

"Suppose that lad that's lying there – " Fagin began.

Sikes turned round to where Noah was sleeping, as if he had not previously observed him. "Well!" he said, resuming his former position.

"Suppose that lad," pursued Fagin, "was to peach – to blow upon us all – first seeking out the right folks for the purpose, and then having a meeting with 'em in the street to paint our likeness, describe every mark that they might know us by, and the crib where we might be most easily taken. Suppose he was to do all this, and besides to blow upon a plant we've all been in, more or less – of his own fancy; not grabbed, trapped, tried, earwigged by the parson and brought to it on bread and water, – but of his own fancy; to please his own taste; stealing out at nights to find those most interested against us, and peaching to them. Do you hear me?" cried the Jew, his eyes flashing with rage. "Suppose he did all this, what then?"

"What then!" replied Sikes; with a tremendous oath. "If he was left alive till I came, I'd grind his skull under the iron heel of my boot into as many grains as there are hairs upon his head."

"What if *I* did it!" cried Fagin almost in a yell. "*I*, that know so much, and could hang so many besides myself!"

"I don't know," replied Sikes, clenching his teeth and turning white at the mere suggestion. "I'd do something in the jail that 'ud get me put in irons; and if I was tried along with you, I'd fall upon you with them in the open court, and beat your brains out afore the people. I should have such strength," muttered the robber, poising his brawny arm, "that I could smash your head as if a loaded waggon had gone over it."

"You would?"

"Would I!" said the housebreaker. "Try me."

"If it was Charley, or the Dodger, or Bet, or –"

"I don't care who," replied Sikes impatiently. "Whoever it was, I'd serve them the same."

Fagin looked hard at the robber; and, motioning him to be silent, stooped over the bed upon the floor, and shook the sleeper to rouse him. Sikes leant forward in his chair: looking on with his hands upon his knees, as if wondering much what all this questioning and preparation was to end in.

"Bolter, Bolter! Poor lad!" said Fagin, looking up with an expression of devilish anticipation, and speaking slowly and with marked emphasis. "He's tired – tired with watching for *her* so long, – watching for *her*, Bill."

"Wot d'ye mean?" asked Sikes, drawing back.

Fagin made no answer, but bending over the sleeper again, hauled him into a sitting posture. When his assumed name had been repeated several times, Noah rubbed his eyes, and, giving a heavy yawn, looked sleepily about him.

"Tell me that again – once again, just for him to hear," said the Jew, pointing to Sikes as he spoke.

"Tell yer what?" asked the sleepy Noah, shaking himself pettishly.

"That about – NANCY," said Fagin, clutching Sikes by the wrist, as if to prevent his leaving the house before he had heard enough. "You followed her?"

"Yes."

"To London Bridge?"

"Yes."

"Where she met two people?"

"So she did."

"A gentleman and a lady that she had gone to of her own accord before, who asked her to give up all her pals, and Monks* first, which she did – and to describe him, which she did – and tell her what house it was that we meet at, and go to, which she did – and where it could be best watched from, which she did – and what time the people went there, which she did. She did all this. She told it all every word without a threat, without a murmur – she did – did she not?" cried Fagin, half mad with fury.

"All right," replied Noah, scratching his head. "That's just what it was!"

"What did they say, about last Sunday?"

"About last Sunday!" replied Noah, considering. "Why I told yer that before."

"Again. Tell it again!" cried Fagin, tightening his grasp on Sikes, and brandishing his other hand aloft, as the foam flew from his lips.

"They asked her," said Noah, who, as he grew more wakeful, seemed to have a dawning perception who Sikes was, "they asked her why she didn't come, last Sunday, as she promised. She said she couldn't."

"Why – why? Tell him that."

"Because she was forcibly kept at home by Bill, the man she had told them of before," replied Noah.

"What more of him?" cried Fagin. "What more of the man she had told them of before? Tell him that, tell him that."

"Why, that she couldn't very easily get out of doors unless he knew where she was going to," said Noah; "and so the first time she went to see the lady, she – ha! ha! ha! it made me laugh when she said it, that it did – she gave him a drink of laudanum*."

"Hell's fire!" cried Sikes, breaking fiercely from the Jew. "Let me go!"

Flinging the old man from him, he rushed from the room, and darted, wildly and furiously, up the stairs.

"Bill, Bill!" cried Fagin, following him hastily. "A word. Only a word."

The word would not have been exchanged, but that the housebreaker was unable to open the door: on which he was expending fruitless oaths and violence, when the Jew came panting up.

"Let me out," said Sikes. "Don't speak to me; it's not safe. Let me out, I say!"

* Monks: Oliver's half-brother, in league with Fagin, who tries to cheat Oliver out of the inheritance left by their father.

* laudanum: a widely used opiate taken as a medicine to dull pain or induce sleep (as here).

"Hear me speak a word," rejoined Fagin, laying his hand upon the lock. "You won't be – "

"Well," replied the other.

"You won't be – too – violent, Bill?"

The day was breaking, and there was light enough for the men to see each other's faces. They exchanged one brief glance; there was a fire in the eyes of both, which could not be mistaken.

"I mean," said Fagin, showing that he felt all disguise was now useless, "not too violent for safety. Be crafty, Bill, and not too bold."

Sikes made no reply; but, pulling open the door, of which Fagin had turned the lock, dashed into the silent streets.

Without one pause, or moment's consideration; without once turning his head to the right or left, or raising his eyes to the sky, or lowering them to the ground, but looking straight before him with savage resolution: his teeth so tightly compressed that the strained jaw seemed starting through his skin; the robber held on his headlong course, nor muttered a word, nor relaxed a muscle, until he reached his own door. He opened it, softly, with a key; strode lightly up the stairs; and entering his own room, double-locked the door, and lifting a heavy table against it, drew back the curtain of the bed.

The girl was lying, half dressed, upon it. He had roused her from her sleep, for she raised herself with a hurried and startled look.

"Get up!" said the man.

"It *is* you, Bill!" said the girl, with an expression of pleasure at his return.

"It is," was the reply. "Get up."

There was a candle burning, but the man hastily drew it from the candlestick, and hurled it under the grate. Seeing the faint light of early day without, the girl rose to undraw the curtain.

"Let it be," said Sikes, thrusting his hand before her. "There's light enough for wot I've got to do."

"Bill," said the girl, in the low voice of alarm, "why do you look like that at me!"

The robber sat regarding her, for a few seconds, with dilated nostrils and heaving breast; and then, grasping her by the head and throat, dragged her into the middle of the room, and looking once towards the door, placed his heavy hand upon her mouth.

"Bill, Bill!" gasped the girl, wrestling with the strength of mortal fear,–"I – I won't scream or cry – not once – hear me – speak to me – tell me what I have done!"

"You know, you she devil!" returned the robber, suppressing his breath. "You were watched tonight; every word you said was heard."

"Then spare my life for the love of Heaven, as I spared yours," rejoined the girl, clinging to him. "Bill, dear Bill, you cannot have the heart to kill me. Oh! think of all I have given up, only this one night, for you. You *shall* have time to think, and save yourself this crime; I will not loose my hold, you cannot throw me off. Bill, Bill, for dear God's sake, for your own, for mine, stop before you spill my blood! I have been true to you, upon my guilty soul I have!"

The man struggled violently to release his arms; but those of the girl were clasped round his, and tear her as he would, he could not tear them away.

"Bill," cried the girl, striving to lay her head upon his breast, "the gentleman and that dear lady, told me tonight of a home in some foreign country where I could end my days in solitude and peace. Let me see them again, and beg them, on my knees, to show the same mercy and goodness to you; and let us both leave this dreadful place, and far apart lead better lives, and forget how we have lived, except in prayers, and never see each other more. It is never too late to repent. They told me so – I feel it now – but we must have time – a little, little time!"

The housebreaker freed one arm, and grasped his pistol. The certainty of immediate detection if he fired, flashed across his mind even in the midst of his fury; and he beat it twice with all the force he could summon, upon the upturned face that almost touched his own.

She staggered and fell: nearly blinded with the blood that rained down from a deep gash in her forehead; but raising herself, with difficulty, on her knees, drew from her bosom a white handkerchief – Rose Maylie's* own – and holding it up, in her folded hands, as high towards Heaven as her feeble strength would allow, breathed one prayer for mercy to her Maker.

It was a ghastly figure to look upon. The murderer staggering backward to the wall, and shutting out the sight with his hand, seized a heavy club and struck her down.

OF ALL BAD DEEDS that, under cover of the darkness, had been committed within wide London's bounds since night hung over it, that was the worst. Of all the horrors that rose with an ill scent upon the morning air, that was the foulest and most cruel.

The sun – the bright sun, that brings back, not light alone, but new life, and hope, and freshness to man – burst upon the crowded city in clear and radiant glory. Through costly-coloured glass and paper-mended window, through cathedral dome and rotten crevice, it shed its equal ray. It lighted up the room where the murdered woman lay. It did. He tried to shut it out, but it would stream in. If the sight had been a

* Rose Maylie: one of Oliver's friends whom Nancy is overheard talking to.

ghastly one in the dull morning, what was it, now, in all that brilliant light!

He had not moved; he had been afraid to stir. There had been a moan and motion of the hand; and, with terror added to rage, he had struck and struck again. Once he threw a rug over it; but it was worse to fancy the eyes, and imagine them moving towards him, than to see them glaring upward, as if watching the reflection of the pool of gore that quivered and danced in the sunlight on the ceiling. He had plucked it off again. And there was the body – mere flesh and blood, no more – but such flesh, and so much blood!

He struck a light, kindled a fire, and thrust the club into it. There was hair upon the end, which blazed and shrunk into a light cinder, and, caught by the air, whirled up the chimney. Even that frightened him, sturdy as he was; but he held the weapon till it broke, and then piled it on the coals to burn away, and smoulder into ashes. He washed himself, and rubbed his clothes; there were spots that would not be removed, but he cut the pieces out, and burnt them. How those stains were dispersed about the room! The very feet of the dog were bloody.

All this time he had never once turned his back upon the corpse; no, not for a moment. Such preparations completed, he moved, backward, towards the door: dragging the dog with him, lest he should soil his feet anew and carry out new evidences of the crime into the streets. He shut the door softly, locked it, took the key, and left the house.

He crossed over, and glanced up at the window, to be sure that nothing was visible from the outside. There was the curtain still drawn, which she would have opened to admit the light she never saw again. It lay nearly under there. *He* knew that. God, how the sun poured down upon the very spot!

The glance was instantaneous. It was a relief to have got free of the room. He whistled on the dog, and walked rapidly away.

He went through Islington; strode up the hill at Highgate on which stands the stone in honour of Whittington; turned down to Highgate Hill, unsteady of purpose, and uncertain where to go; struck off to the right again, almost as soon as he began to descend it; and taking the footpath across the fields, skirted Caen Wood, and so came out on Hampstead Heath. Traversing the hollow by the Vale of Health, he mounted the opposite bank, and crossing the road which joins the villages of Hampstead and Highgate, made along the remaining portion of the heath to the fields at North End, in one of which he laid himself down under a hedge, and slept.

Soon he was up again, and away, – not far into the country, but back towards London by the high-road – then back again – then over another part of the same ground as he already traversed – then wandering up

A London slum

and down in fields, and lying on ditches' brinks to rest, and starting up to make for some other spot, and do the same, and ramble on again.

Where could he go, that was near and not too public, to get some meat and drink? Hendon. That was a good place, not far off, and out of most people's way. Thither he directed his steps, – running sometimes, and sometimes, with a strange perversity, loitering at a snail's pace, or stopping altogether and idly breaking the hedges with his stick. But when he got there, all the people he met – the very children at the doors – seemed to view him with suspicion. Back he turned again, without the courage to purchase bit or drop, though he had tasted no food for many hours; and once more he lingered on the Heath, uncertain where to go.

He wandered over miles and miles of ground, and still came back to the old place. Morning and noon had passed, and the day was on the wane, and still he rambled to and fro, and up and down, and round and round, and still lingered about the same spot. At last he got away, and shaped his course for Hatfield.

It was nine o'clock at night, when the man, quite tired out, and the dog, limping and lame from the unaccustomed exercise, turned down the hill by the church of the quiet village, and plodding along the little street, crept into a small public-house, whose scanty light had guided them to the spot. There was a fire in the tap-room, and some country-labourers were drinking before it. They made room for the stranger, but he sat down in the farthest corner, and ate and drank alone, or rather with his dog, to whom he cast a morsel of food from time to time.

Oliver Twist, *Chapters 47 and 48*

Sikes at bay

The hue and cry raised against Bill Sikes after the savage murder of his lover, Nancy, forces him to run to ground on Jacob's Island, a slum area and a haunt of criminals in the Thames, opposite Bermondsey. Sikes is at bay with the large angry crowd at his heels and no way of escape.

"THE TIDE," cried the murderer, as he staggered back into the room, and shut the faces out, "the tide was in as I came up. Give me a rope, a long rope. They're all in front. I may drop into the Folly Ditch, and clear off that way. Give me a rope, or I shall do three more murders and kill myself."

The panic-stricken men pointed to where such articles were kept; the murderer, hastily selecting the longest and strongest cord, hurried up to the house-top.

All the windows in the rear of the house had been long ago bricked up, except one small trap in the room where the boy* was locked, and that was too small even for the passage of his body. But, from this aperture, he had never ceased to call on those without, to guard the back; and thus, when the murderer emerged at last on the house-top by the door in the roof, a loud shout proclaimed the fact to those in front, who immediately began to pour round, pressing upon each other in an unbroken stream.

He planted a board, which he had carried up with him for the purpose, so firmly against the door that it must be matter of great difficulty to open it from the inside; and creeping over the tiles, looked over the low parapet.

The water was out, and the ditch a bed of mud.

The crowd had been hushed during these few moments, watching his motions and doubtful of his purpose, but the instant they perceived it and knew it was defeated, they raised a cry of triumphant execration to which all their previous shouting had been whispers. Again and again it rose. Those who were at too great a distance to know its meaning, took up the sound; it echoed and re-echoed; it seemed as though the whole city had poured its population out to curse him.

On pressed the people from the front – on, on, on, in a strong strug-

* the boy: Charley Bates, a young delinquent whom Sikes locks up. Charley has tried to give Sikes away to the pursuing crowd.

The last chance

gling current of angry faces, with here and there a glaring torch to light them up, and show them out in all their wrath and passion. The houses on the opposite side of the ditch had been entered by the mob; sashes were thrown up, or torn bodily out; there were tiers and tiers of faces in every window; cluster upon cluster of people clinging to every housetop. Each little bridge (and there were three in sight) bent beneath the weight of the crowd upon it. Still the current poured on to find some nook or hole from which to vent their shouts, and only for an instant see the wretch.

"They have him now," cried a man on the nearest bridge. "Hurrah!"

The crowd grew light with uncovered heads; and again the shout uprose.

"I will give fifty pounds," cried an old gentleman from the same quarter, "to the man who takes him alive. I will remain here, till he comes to ask me for it."

There was another roar. At this moment the word was passed among the crowd that the door was forced at last, and that he who had first called for the ladder had mounted into the room. The stream abruptly turned, as this intelligence ran from mouth to mouth; and the people at the windows, seeing those upon the bridges pouring back, quitted their stations, and running into the street, joined the concourse that now thronged pell-mell to the spot they had left: each man crushing and striving with his neighbour, and all panting with impatience to get near the door, and look upon the criminal as the officers brought him out. The cries and shrieks of those who were pressed almost to suffocation, or trampled down and trodden under foot in the confusion, were dreadful; the narrow ways were completely blocked up; and at this time, between the rush of some to regain the space in front of the house, and the unavailing struggle of others to extricate themselves from the mass, the immediate attention was distracted from the murderer, although the universal eagerness for his capture was, if possible, increased.

The man had shrunk down, thoroughly quelled by the ferocity of the crowd, and the impossibility of escape; but seeing this sudden change with no less rapidity than it had occurred, he sprang upon his feet, determined to make one last effort for his life by dropping into the ditch, and, at the risk of being stifled, endeavouring to creep away in the darkness and confusion.

Roused into new strength and energy, and stimulated by the noise within the house which announced that an entrance had really been effected, he set his foot against the stack of chimneys, fastened one end of the rope tightly and firmly round it, and with the other made a strong running noose by the aid of his hands and teeth almost in a second. He could let himself down by the cord to within a less distance of the ground than his own height, and had his knife ready in his hand to cut it then and drop.

At the very instant when he brought the loop over his head previous to slipping it beneath his arm-pits, and when the old gentleman before-mentioned (who had clung so tight to the railing of the bridge as to resist the force of the crowd, and retain his position) earnestly warned those about him that the man was about to lower himself down – at that very instant the murderer, looking behind him on the roof, threw his arms above his head, and uttered a yell of terror.

"The eyes again!"* he cried in an unearthly screech.

Staggering as if struck by lightning, he lost his balance and tumbled over the parapet. The noose was on his neck. It ran up with his weight, tight as a bowstring, and swift as the arrow it speeds. He fell for five-and-thirty feet. There was a sudden jerk, a terrific convulsion of the limbs; and there he hung, with the open knife clenched in his stiffening hand.

The old chimney quivered with the shock, but stood it bravely. The murderer swung lifeless against the wall; and a boy, thrusting aside the dangling body which obscured his view, called to the people to come and take him out, for God's sake.

Oliver Twist, *Chapter 50*

* "The eyes again!": Sikes imagines Nancy's eyes looking at him: she loved him even as he murdered her.

Pursued

*Dickens has different ways of punishing his villains. In **Dombey and Son**, James Carker, bitter at his subordination as a manager in the firm that gives the novel its title, attempts to ruin the business and does succeed in destroying his employer's marriage. But this is at the cost of becoming an outcast and fugitive himself. Pursued by his employer, Mr. Dombey, Carker feels the hopelessness of his position as he seeks refuge in a country tavern near a railway station.*

But, as if there were a curse upon him that he should never rest again, his drowsy senses would not lose their consciousness. He had no more influence with them in this regard, than if they had been another man's. It was not that they forced him to take note of present sounds and objects, but that they would not be diverted from the whole hurried vision of his journey. It was constantly before him all at once. She* stood there, with her dark disdainful eyes again upon him; and he was riding on nevertheless, through town and country, light and darkness, wet weather and dry, over road and pavement, hill and valley, height and hollow, jaded and scared by the monotony of bells and wheels, and horses' feet, and no rest.

"What day is this?" he asked of the waiter, who was making preparations for his dinner.

"Day, Sir?"

"Is it Wednesday?"

"Wednesday, Sir? No, Sir. Thursday, Sir."

"I forgot. How goes the time? My watch is unwound."

"Wants a few minutes of five o'clock, Sir. Been travelling a long time, Sir, perhaps?"

"Yes."

"By rail, Sir?"

"Yes."

"Very confusing, Sir. Not much in the habit of travelling by rail myself, Sir, but gentlemen frequently say so."

"Do many gentlemen come here?"

"Pretty well, Sir, in general. Nobody here at present. Rather slack just now, Sir. Everything *is* slack, Sir."

* She: Mr. Dombey's wife for whom Carker nurses an unrequited passion

He made no answer; but had risen into a sitting posture on the sofa where he had been lying, and leaned forward with an arm on each knee, staring at the ground. He could not master his own attention for a minute together. It rushed away where it would, but it never, for an instant, lost itself in sleep.

He drank a quantity of wine after dinner, in vain. No such artificial means would bring sleep to his eyes. His thoughts, more incoherent, dragged him more unmercifully after them – as if a wretch, condemned to such expiation, were drawn at the heels of wild horses. No oblivion, and no rest.

How long he sat, drinking and brooding, and being dragged in imagination hither and thither, no one could have told less correctly than he. But he knew that he had been sitting a long time by candle-light, when he started up and listened, in a sudden terror.

For now, indeed, it was no fancy. The ground shook, the house rattled, the fierce impetuous rush was in the air! He felt it come up, and go darting by; and even when he had hurried to the window, and saw what it was, he stood, shrinking from it, as if it were not safe to look.

A curse upon the fiery devil, thundering along so smoothly, tracked through the distant valley by a glare of light and lurid smoke, and gone! He felt as if he had been plucked out of its path, and saved from being torn asunder. It made him shrink and shudder even now, when its faintest hum was hushed, and when the lines of iron road he could trace in the moonlight, running to a point, were as empty and as silent as a desert.

Unable to rest, and irresistibly attracted – or he thought so – to this road, he went out and lounged on the brink of it, marking the way the train had gone, by the yet smoking cinders that were lying in its track. After a lounge of some half hour in the direction by which it had disappeared, he turned and walked the other way – still keeping to the brink of the road – past the inn garden, and a long way down; looking curiously at the bridges, signals, lamps, and wondering when another Devil would come by.

A trembling of the ground, and quick vibration in his ears; a distant shriek; a dull light advancing, quickly changed to two red eyes, and a fierce fire, dropping glowing coals; an irresistible bearing on of a great roaring and dilating mass; a high wind, and a rattle – another come and gone, and he holding to a gate, as if to save himself!

He waited for another, and for another. He walked back to his former point, and back again to that, and still, through the wearisome vision of his journey, looked for these approaching monsters. He loitered about the station, waiting until one should stay to call there; and when one did, and was detached for water, he stood parallel with it, watching its heavy wheels and brazen front, and thinking what a cruel power and might it had. Ugh! To see the great wheels slowly turning, and to think of being run down and crushed!

Disordered with wine and want of rest – that want which nothing, although he was so weary, would appease – these ideas and objects assumed a diseased importance in his thoughts. When he went back to his room, which was not until near midnight, they still haunted him, and he sat listening for the coming of another.

So in his bed, whither he repaired with no hope of sleep. He still lay listening; and when he felt the trembling and vibration, got up and went to the window, to watch (as he could from its position) the dull light changing to the two red eyes, and the fierce fire dropping glowing coals, and the rush of the giant as it fled past, and the track of glare and smoke along the valley. Then he would glance in the direction by which he intended to depart at sunrise, as there was no rest for him there; and would lie down again, to be troubled by the vision of his journey, and the old monotony of bells and wheels and horses' feet, until another came. This lasted all night. So far from resuming the mastery of himself, he seemed, if possible, to lose it more and more, as the night crept on. When the dawn appeared, he was still tormented with thinking, still postponing thought until he should be in a better state; the past, present, and future, all floated confusedly before him, and he had lost all power of looking steadily at any one of them.

"At what time," he asked the man who had waited on him over-night, now entering with a candle, "do I leave here, did you say?"

"About a quarter after four, Sir. Express comes through at four, Sir. It don't stop."

He passed his hand across his throbbing head, and looked at his watch. Nearly half-past three.

"Nobody going with you, Sir, probably," observed the man. "Two gentlemen here, Sir, but they're waiting for the train to London."

"I thought you said there was nobody here," said Carker, turning upon him with the ghost of his old smile, when he was angry or suspicious.

"Not then, Sir. Two gentlemen came in the night by the short train that stops here, Sir. Warm water, Sir?"

"No; and take away the candle. There's day enough for me."

Having thrown himself upon the bed, half-dressed, he was at the window as the man left the room. The cold light of morning had succeeded to night, and there was already, in the sky, the red suffusion of the coming sun. He bathed his head and face with water – there was no cooling influence in it for him – hurriedly put on his clothes, paid what he owed, and went out.

The air struck chill and comfortless, as it breathed upon him. There was a heavy dew; and, hot as he was, it made him shiver. After a glance at the place where he had walked last night, and at the signal-lights burning feebly in the morning, and bereft of their significance, he turned to where the sun was rising, and beheld it, in its glory, as it broke upon the scene.

So awful, so transcendent in its beauty, so divinely solemn. As he cast his faded eyes upon it, when it rose, tranquil and serene, unmoved by all the wrong and wickedness on which its beams had shone since the beginning of the world, who shall say that some weak sense of virtue upon Earth, and its reward in Heaven, did not manifest itself, even to him? If ever he remembered sister or brother with a touch of tenderness and remorse, who shall say it was not then?

He needed some such touch then. Death was on him. He was marked off from the living world, and going down into his grave.

He paid the money for his journey to the country-place he had thought of; and was walking to and fro, alone, looking along the lines of iron, across the valley in one direction, and towards a dark bridge near at hand in the other; when, turning in his walk, where it was bounded by one end of the wooden stage on which he paced up and down, he saw the man from whom he had fled, emerging from the door by which he himself had entered there. And their eyes met.

In the quick unsteadiness of the surprise, he staggered, and slipped on to the road below him. But recovering his feet immediately, he stepped back a pace or two upon that road, to interpose some wider space between them, and looked at his pursuer, breathing short and quick.

He heard a shout – another – saw the face change from its vindictive passion to a faint sickness and terror – felt the earth tremble – knew in a moment that the rush was come – uttered a shriek – looked round – saw the red eyes, bleared and dim in the daylight, close upon him – was beaten down, caught up, and whirled away upon a jagged mill, that spun him round and round, and struck him limb from limb, and licked his stream of life up with its fiery heat, and cast his mutilated fragments in the air.

When the traveller, who had been recognised, recovered from a swoon, he saw them bringing from a distance something covered that lay heavy and still upon a board, between four men, and saw that others drove some dogs away that sniffed upon the road, and soaked his blood up with a train of ashes.

Dombey and Son, *Chapter 55*

Death cell

The "Crime and Punishment" section of this book began with Newgate Prison and it seems right to end with it. What Dickens imagines in one of his **Sketches** *he makes even more powerful in the chapter of* **Oliver Twist** *in which Fagin, the organiser of a gang of juvenile pickpockets, is tried, condemned to death and awaits public hanging.*

THE COURT was paved, from floor to roof, with human faces. Inquisitive and eager eyes peered from every inch of space. From the rail before the dock, away into the sharpest angle of the smallest corner in the galleries, all looks were fixed upon one man – the Jew. Before him and behind: above, below, on the right and on the left: he seemed to stand surrounded by a firmament, all bright with gleaming eyes.

He stood there, in all this glare of living light, with one hand resting on the wooden slab before him, the other held to his ear, and his head thrust forward to enable him to catch with greater distinctness every word that fell from the presiding judge, who was delivering his charge to the jury. At times, he turned his eyes sharply upon them to observe the effect of the slightest featherweight in his favour; and when the points against him were stated with terrible distinctness, looked towards his counsel, in mute appeal that he would, even then, urge something in his behalf. Beyond these manifestations of anxiety, he stirred not hand or foot. He had scarcely moved since the trial began; and now that the judge ceased to speak, he still remained in the same strained attitude of close attention, with his gaze bent on him, as though he listened still.

A slight bustle in the court recalled him to himself. Looking round, he saw that the jurymen had turned together, to consider of their verdict. As his eyes wandered to the gallery, he could see the people rising above each other to see his face: some hastily applying their glasses to their eyes, and others whispering their neighbours with looks expressive of abhorrence. A few there were, who seemed unmindful of him, and looked only to the jury, in impatient wonder how they could delay. But in no one face – not even among the women, of whom there were many there – could he read the faintest sympathy with himself, or any feeling but one of all-absorbing interest that he should be condemned.

As he saw all this in one bewildered glance, the death-like stillness came again, and looking back, he saw that the jurymen had turned towards the judge. Hush!

They only sought permission to retire.

He looked, wistfully, into their faces, one by one, when they passed out, as though to see which way the greater number leant; but that was fruitless. The jailer touched him on the shoulder. He followed mechanically to the end of the dock, and sat down on a chair. The man pointed it out, or he would not have seen it.

He looked up into the gallery again. Some of the people were eating, and some fanning themselves with handkerchiefs; for the crowded place was very hot. There was one young man sketching his face in a little note-book. He wondered whether it was like, and looked on when the artist broke his pencil-point, and made another with his knife, as any idle spectator might have done.

In the same way, when he turned his eyes towards the judge, his mind began to busy itself with the fashion of his dress, and what it cost, and how he put it on. There was an old fat gentleman on the bench, too, who had gone out, some half an hour before, and now come back. He wondered within himself whether this man had been to get his dinner, what he had had, and where he had had it; and pursued this train of careless thought until some new object caught his eye and roused another.

Not that, all this time, his mind was, for an instant, free from one oppressive overwhelming sense of the grave that opened at his feet; it was ever present to him, but in a vague and general way, and he could not fix his thoughts upon it. Thus, even while he trembled, and turned burning hot at the idea of speedy death, he fell to counting the iron spikes before him, and wondering how the head of one had been broken off, and whether they would mend it, or leave it as it was. Then, he thought of all the horrors of the gallows and the scaffold – and stopped to watch a man sprinkling the floor to cool it – and then went on to think again.

At length there was a cry of silence, and a breathless look from all towards the door. The jury returned, and passed him close. He could glean nothing from their faces; they might as well have been of stone. Perfect stillness ensued – not a rustle – not a breath – Guilty.

The building rang with a tremendous shout, and another, and another, and then it echoed loud groans, then gathered strength as they swelled out, like angry thunder. It was a peal of joy from the populace outside, greeting the news that he would die on Monday.

The noise subsided, and he was asked if he had anything to say why sentence of death should not be passed upon him. He had resumed his listening attitude, and looked intently at his questioner while the demand was made; but it was twice repeated before he seemed to hear it, and then he only muttered that he was an old man – an old man – an old man – and so, dropping into a whisper, was silent again.

The judge assumed the black cap, and the prisoner still stood with the same air and gesture. A woman in the gallery uttered some exclamation, called forth by this dread solemnity; he looked hastily up as if angry at the interruption, and bent forward yet more attentively. The address was solemn and impressive; the sentence fearful to hear. But he stood, like a marble figure, without the motion of a nerve. His haggard face was still thrust forward, his under-jaw hanging down, and his eyes staring out before him, when the jailer put his hand upon his arm, and beckoned him away. He gazed stupidly about him for an instant, and obeyed.

They led him through a paved room under the court, where some prisoners were waiting till their turns came, and others were talking to their friends, who crowded round a grate which looked into the open yard. There was nobody there, to speak to *him*; but, as he passed, the prisoners fell back to render him more visible to the people who were clinging to the bars: and they assailed him with opprobrious names, and screeched and hissed. He shook his fist, and would have spat upon them; but his conductors hurried him on, through a gloomy passage lighted by a few dim lamps, into the interior of the prison.

Here, he was searched, that he might not have about him the means of anticipating the law; this ceremony performed, they led him to one of the condemned cells, and left him there – alone.

He sat down on a stone bench opposite the door, which served for a seat and bedstead; and casting his blood-shot eyes upon the ground, tried to collect his thoughts. After a while, he began to remember a few disjointed fragments of what the judge had said, though it had seemed to him, at the time, that he could not hear a word. These gradually fell into their proper places, and by degrees suggested more: so that in a little time he had the whole, almost as it was delivered. To be hanged by the neck, till he was dead – that was the end. To be hanged by the neck till he was dead.

As it came on very dark, he began to think of all the men he had known who had died upon the scaffold; some of them through his means. They rose up, in such quick succession, that he could hardly count them. He had seen some of them die, – and had joked too, because they died with prayers upon their lips. With what a rattling noise the drop went down; and how suddenly they changed, from strong and vigorous men to dangling heaps of clothes!

Some of them might have inhabited that very cell – sat upon that very spot. It was very dark; why didn't they bring a light? The cell had been built for many years. Scores of men must have passed their last hours

Fagin in the Condemned Cell

there. It was like sitting in a vault strewn with dead bodies – the cap, the noose, the pinioned arms, the faces that he knew, even beneath that hideous veil. – Light, light!

At length, when his hands were raw with beating against the heavy door and walls, two men appeared: one bearing a candle, which he thrust into an iron candlestick fixed against the wall: the other dragging in a mattress on which to pass the night; for the prisoner was to be left alone no more.

Then came night – dark, dismal, silent night. Other watchers are glad to hear the church-clocks strike, for they tell of life and coming day. To the Jew they brought despair. The boom of every iron bell came laden with the one, deep, hollow sound – Death. What availed the noise and bustle of cheerful morning, which penetrated even there, to him? It was another form of knell, with mockery added to the warning.

The day passed off. Day? There was no day; it was gone as soon as come – and night came on again; night so long, and yet so short; long in its dreadful silence, and short in its fleeting hours. At one time he raved and blasphemed; and at another howled and tore his hair. Venerable men of his own persuasion had come to pray beside him, but he had driven them away with curses. They renewed their charitable efforts, and he beat them off.

Saturday night. He had only one night more to live. And as he thought of this, the day broke – Sunday.

It was not until the night of this last awful day, that a withering sense of his helpless, desperate state came in its full intensity upon his blighted soul; not that he had ever held any defined or positive hope of mercy, but that he had never been able to consider more than the dim probability of dying so soon. He had spoken little to either of the two men, who relieved each other in their attendance upon him; and they, for their parts, made no effort to rouse his attention. He had sat there, awake, but dreaming. Now, he started up, every minute, and with gasping mouth and burning skin, hurried to and fro, in such a paroxysm of fear and wrath that even they – used to such sights – recoiled from him with horror. He grew so terrible, at last, in all the tortures of his evil conscience, that one man could not bear to sit there, eyeing him alone; and so the two kept watch together.

He cowered down upon his stone bed, and thought of the past. He had been wounded with some missiles from the crowd on the day of his capture, and his head was bandaged with a linen cloth. His red hair hung down upon his bloodless face; his beard was torn, and twisted into knots; his eyes shone with a terrible light; his unwashed flesh crackled with the fever that burnt him up. Eight – nine – ten. If it was not a trick to frighten him, and those were the real hours treading on each other's heels, where would he be, when they came round again! Eleven! Another struck, before the voice of the previous hour had ceased to vibrate. At eight, he would be the only mourner in his own funeral train; at eleven –

Those dreadful walls of Newgate, which have hidden so much misery and such unspeakable anguish, not only from the eyes, but too often, and too long, from the thoughts, of men, never held so dread a spectacle as that. The few who lingered as they passed, and wondered what the man was doing who was to be hanged tomorrow, would have slept but ill that night, if they could have seen him.

From early in the evening until nearly midnight, little groups of two and three presented themselves at the lodge-gate, and inquired, with anxious faces, whether any reprieve had been received. These being answered in the negative, communicated the welcome intelligence to clusters in the street, who pointed out to one another the door from which he must come out, and showed where the scaffold would be built, and, walking with unwilling steps away, turned back to conjure up the scene. By degrees they fell off, one by one; and, for an hour, in the dead of night, the street was left to solitude and darkness.

The space before the prison was cleared, and a few strong barriers, painted black, had been already thrown across the road to break the pressure of the expected crowd, when Mr. Brownlow* and Oliver appeared at the wicket, and presented an order of admission to the prisoner, signed by one of the sheriffs. They were immediately admitted into the lodge.

"Is the young gentleman to come too, sir?" said the man whose duty it was to conduct them. "It's not a sight for children, sir."

"It is not indeed, my friend," rejoined Mr. Brownlow; "but my business with this man is intimately connected with him; and as this child has seen him in the full career of his success and villainy, I think it as well – even at the cost of some pain and fear – that he should see him now."

These few words had been said apart, so as to be inaudible to Oliver. The man touched his hat; and glancing at Oliver with some curiosity, opened another gate, opposite to that by which they had entered, and led them on, through dark and winding ways, towards the cells.

"This," said the man, stopping in a gloomy passage where a couple of workmen were making some preparations in profound silence – "this is the place he passes through. If you step this way, you can see the door he goes out at."

He led them into a stone kitchen, fitted with coppers for dressing the prison food, and pointed to a door. There was an open grating above it, through which came the sound of men's voices, mingled with the noise of hammering, and the throwing down of boards. They were putting up the scaffold.

Oliver Twist, *Chapter 52*

* Mr. Brownlow: friend and benefactor of Oliver Twist